A VISTAS OF SCIENCE BOOK

Spac

By JAMES J. HAGGERTY, JR.
Editor, *Aerospace Year Book*
Washington, D.C.

STUDENT ACTIVITIES By JOHN H. WOODBURN
Science Teacher, Walter Johnson High School
Rockville, Maryland

Spacecraft Advisory Group

Research Scientist: JOHN F. CLARK
Head, Geophysics Department
National Aeronautics and Space Administration
Washington, D.C.

Science Educator: ORVAL ULRY
Department of Education
University of Maryland
College Park, Maryland

Science Teacher: JOHN H. WOODBURN
Walter Johnson High School
Rockville, Maryland

Produced as a joint project of the NATIONAL SCIENCE
TEACHERS ASSOCIATION and the NATIONAL AERO-
NAUTICS AND SPACE ADMINISTRATION. Published by
SCHOLASTIC BOOK SERVICES, A Division of Scholastic
Magazines, Inc., New York, New York.

Vistas of Science Advisory Board

ROBERT BINGER
Supervisor, Science Education
Department of Education
State of Florida, Tallahassee

GRAHAM DuSHANE
Editor of *Science*
American Association for
    Advancement of Science,
Washington, D.C.

MASON R. BOUDRYE
Executive Secretary
Minnesota Academy of Science
St. Paul, Minnesota

F. L. FITZPATRICK
Professor of Natural Sciences
Columbia University—and
    Head, Science Department
Teachers College, Columbia
University, New York City

R. WILL BURNETT
Professor of Science Education
University of Illinois
Urbana, Illinois

SISTER M. GABRIELLE
Principal
Holy Trinity High School
Hartford, Connecticut

HUGH ODISHAW
Executive Director
Space Science Board
National Academy of Sciences
National Research Council
Washington, D.C.

Copyright © 1962 by the National Science Teachers Association, Inc.
All rights reserved. Published by Scholastic Book Services.

2nd printing .... May 1962

Manufactured in the U.S.A.
Library of Congress Catalog Card Number: 62-13273

NATIONAL SCIENCE TEACHERS ASSOCIATION
1201 Sixteenth Street, N. W., Washington 6, D.C.

A Department of the National Education Association
An Affiliate of the American Association for the Advancement of Science

Exciting discoveries, major breakthroughs, and important new applications continue to widen our vistas of science, engineering, and technology, producing an impact on society which touches every individual. These expanding frontiers inspire large numbers of our youth to consider careers in science, and thoughtful persons of all ages seek a better understanding of the scientific-technological society in which we live. As a result, there is an insatiable demand for current, accurate scientific information. To fill this pressing need, the National Science Teachers Association has conceived and developed the VISTAS OF SCIENCE series. In so doing, NSTA advances its own central purpose: improvement of the teaching of science. In addition, VISTAS books provide scientific background for those who would be well-informed, responsible citizens.

Designed at the request of students and teachers, the series is produced under the guidance of an experienced Advisory Board (see facing page). Each book is concerned with a specific science area, such as spacecraft, oceanography, astronomy, the cell, genetics, measurement.

Three types of information characterize VISTAS OF SCIENCE books: presentation of subject matter, research frontiers and methods, and student activities. VISTAS are science resource and enrichment literature that is sound and challenging. Written for junior and senior high school students, the VISTAS are of interest and value to teachers and other adults as well.

Sponsors of VISTAS books include governmental agencies, professional societies, and industrial organizations. These groups help to support the program financially and cooperate to insure that the manuscripts are developed as objective, authentic explorations of particular science areas.

The authors are scientists, science writers, and classroom teachers of outstanding experience, background, and communicative skills. Often a combination of authors develops the manuscript — a scientist or science writer prepares the main text, and a classroom teacher prepares the student activity section.

An advisory group, composed of a research scientist, a science educator, and a science teacher, assists in the planning and reviewing of each manuscript. These advisers represent three groups vitally concerned with providing sound education in science.

The VISTAS OF SCIENCE books are made available by the publisher through its school book-club programs and by individual purchase. One copy of each VISTA is provided free to all school science clubs enrolled in NSTA's Future Scientists of America organization.

The VISTAS program, through the cooperative efforts of authors, advisory groups, sponsors, NSTA, and the publisher, makes possible low-cost, versatile science libraries in the science classrooms of the nation's schools and encourages individual students to plan home science libraries as well.

The suggestions and comments of students, teachers, and other readers of VISTAS OF SCIENCE books will be welcome.

Robert H. Carleton
Executive Secretary, NSTA

Marjorie Gardner
Director, VISTAS OF SCIENCE

CONTENTS

The "Why" of Space Exploration

WILLIAM MEYERRIECKS

IN this twentieth century, we are privileged to witness the first steps toward realization of an age-old dream: the exploration of space.

Already, in the first few years of the Space Age, man has been able to penetrate the layer of atmosphere which surrounds his planet and to venture briefly into space. Scores of man-made objects have been thrust into space, some of them to roam the solar system forever.

Behind each space mission are years of patient research, thousands of man-hours of labor, and large sums of money. Because the sums involved are so enormous, the question is frequently asked, "Is it worth it?" Many people want to know what return this huge investment will bring to mankind.

The return on the investment is *knowledge.* The accumulation of knowledge over the centuries has made possible our advanced way of life. As we unlock more and more of the secrets of the universe through space exploration, we add new volumes to the encyclopedia of man's knowledge. This will be applied to the benefit of mankind.

For the practical-minded, there are concrete benefits to our way of life. Although we are still in the Stone Age of space exploration, a number of immediate applications of space technology are already apparent.

CHAPTER 1

For instance, imagine the benefits of an absolutely perfect system of predicting the weather. Or, going a step further, even *changing* the weather. And wouldn't it be fascinating to watch the next Olympic games, telecast from Tokyo, on your TV set? These are just a few of the practical benefits made possible by space technology.

The Meteorological Satellite

Let us consider the weather satellite. The weatherman has been the butt of many a joke about faulty predictions. But it is not his ability to predict weather which has been at fault; rather, it is lack of sufficient information upon which to base his predictions. Regular weather observations cover only about one fifth of the Earth's surface. Too frequently the forecaster is unaware of changing conditions which might completely alter his prediction.

An Earth satellite equipped with television can provide a precise picture of cloud and storm patterns around the globe. It can circle the Earth every ninety minutes and transmit images of the clouds which forecasters can analyze and interpret for more accurate weather predictions. Think of the advantages of precise weather information to people engaged in air transportation or agriculture, to the sponsors of outdoor events, and to homeowners in the paths of destructive storms. And, once accurate forecasting is available, we may be able to "do something about the weather."

The Communications Satellite

Another type of spacecraft which offers great potential benefit is the communications satellite. Signals can be directed to the satellite from one point on Earth and rebroadcast to another point or to another satellite.

The possibilities of communications satellites are vast, particularly in the field of transoceanic messages, a good por-

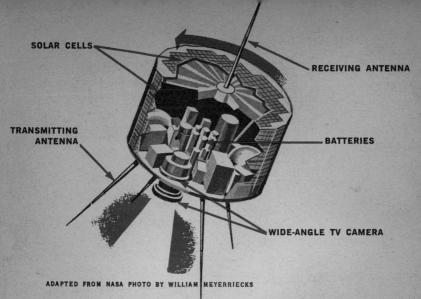

ADAPTED FROM NASA PHOTO BY WILLIAM MEYERRIECKS

SOLAR CELLS

RECEIVING ANTENNA

TRANSMITTING ANTENNA

BATTERIES

WIDE-ANGLE TV CAMERA

"Applied" satellite; TIROS meteorological spacecraft. Its television cameras survey Earth's cloud cover.

tion of which are now handled by cable. Because the quantity of transoceanic messages has increased almost to the limitations of the present cable system, even a projected expansion of the system may not be adequate in a few years. The communications satellite may replace the cable and microwave devices, and solve a major problem by opening up more channels, permitting less expensive and more rapid message transmissions. This will have great impact on foreign trade. The communications satellite is also the answer to long-awaited international television, which might never come to pass if we had to rely on cable systems of insufficient capacity.

Spacecraft as Navigation Aids

The spacecraft also offers potential in the field of navigation, as an absolutely reliable means of fixing the position of a surface ship, a submarine, or an airplane. Accurately placed in a predetermined orbit and equipped with radio transmitters, satellites would become artificial "stars" by which vessels or aircraft could navigate. Ships and planes would receive signals from satellites. Since the satellites would always be in a known position, a navigator could easily determine his craft's position in relation to that of the man-made "stars." The navigation satellite, efficient even on the darkest of nights, probably will replace most of the navigation aids used today.

The science of geodesy — the study of the curvature, shape, and dimensions of the Earth — offers still another application for spacecraft. A satellite could provide a base point in space from which we on Earth could measure precise distances between land masses and pinpoint exact locations of tiny islands. Even with today's advanced techniques, highly accurate measurements of this type are not possible.

These are just some examples of practical applications of space technology. Others will become apparent as the science

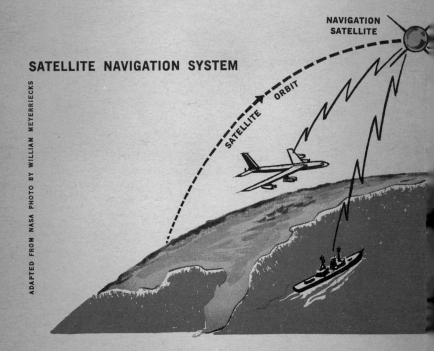

SATELLITE NAVIGATION SYSTEM

NAVIGATION SATELLITE

SATELLITE ORBIT

ADAPTED FROM NASA PHOTO BY WILLIAM MEYERRIECKS

of space exploration advances. It must be stressed, however, that the primary reason for exploring space is to gain knowledge. These practical applications are by-products of basic research, the goal of which is to *add to man's knowledge* without immediate regard for the manner in which the knowledge may be employed.

Observatories in Orbit

Of profound importance from the scientific standpoint is accurate information on our solar system — its history and its place in our galaxy. Spacecraft provide, for the first time, precise tools for acquiring such information. Examples of various spacecraft will soon be at work in this field, for it is planned to send a series of observatories into space within the next few years.

These spacecraft observatories, equipped with a wide variety of scientific instruments, will orbit the Earth, collecting

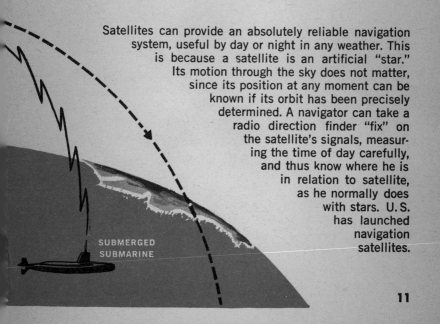

Satellites can provide an absolutely reliable navigation system, useful by day or night in any weather. This is because a satellite is an artificial "star." Its motion through the sky does not matter, since its position at any moment can be known if its orbit has been precisely determined. A navigator can take a radio direction finder "fix" on the satellite's signals, measuring the time of day carefully, and thus know where he is in relation to satellite, as he normally does with stars. U.S. has launched navigation satellites.

SUBMERGED
SUBMARINE

data about the solar system. There are three basic types of orbiting observatories: the orbiting geophysical observatory, the orbiting astronomical observatory, and the orbiting solar observatory.

The orbiting geophysical observatory, as it orbits around our planet, will study the characteristics of Earth and near-space. On one type of mission, it will go into an eccentric orbit which will take it at times 70,000 miles from Earth and at other times as close as 175 miles, permitting collection of a wide range of data. On another mission, it will orbit about the North and South Poles, at altitudes of 175 to 700 miles, collecting other data and studying, in particular, the unexplored regions of Earth's atmosphere above the poles.

The orbiting astronomical observatory will study the sun, stars, and planets. Equipped with large telescopes and other scientific instruments, it will orbit the Earth at about 500 miles altitude, high above the dense lower layers of atmosphere which distort observations made from the surface of the Earth.

The orbiting solar observatory will orbit at about 300 miles altitude. Its battery of instruments will study the sun and its phenomena, in particular the various forms of solar radiation.

These orbiting observatories and other, more specialized, scientific spacecraft will contribute in great measure to our knowledge of the solar system. How will that benefit mankind? There may be no immediate practical application for the knowledge we gain about our Earth's origins, but enlightenment is a goal in itself.

History
of
Space Flight

O N October 4, 1957, the world was electrified by the news
that the Soviet Union had succeeded in placing a man-
made object in orbit about the Earth. Although that date is
accepted as the formal beginning of space flight, a complete
history of the subject starts at a much earlier date.

The exploration of space began long before man had
the means to send objects into space. It started when man
first realized that the planet he inhabited was not the only
body in space. The first such recorded belief can be found in
the writings of Plutarch, who lived in the first century A.D.

The first major step in theoretical space exploration
occurred in the sixteenth century with the invention of the
telescope. During the sixteenth and seventeenth centuries, astronomers such as Copernicus, Johannes Kepler, and Galileo
charted the motion of celestial bodies and laid the groundwork
for modern space research.

Before man could explore space itself, he needed a means
for thrusting his instruments beyond Earth's atmosphere. It

CHAPTER 2

WIDE WORLD

Prime problem of space exploration is getting "up" there. First step was made by U.S. scientist Dr. Robert Goddard, who fired first liquid-fueled rocket, on March 16, 1926.

had to be a type of propulsion which did not need air for its operation, since in space there is little or no air. This was a characteristic of the rocket engine. Rockets existed centuries before the first spacecraft went into orbit, but in a primitive form hardly adaptable to space exploration.

As early as A.D. 1232 the Chinese had used rockets, or "arrows of flying fire," against invading Mongols. Rockets were used as weapons for centuries thereafter, until the latter part of the nineteenth century, when the accuracy of conventional artillery put the erratic rocket on the shelf. Over the centuries, the rocket went through several stages of development, but it never became more than a short-range method of propulsion.

Dr. Goddard and the Rocket

Not until the twentieth century were the first steps taken toward developing the rocket as a means of space propulsion. The honor fell to an American physicist, Dr. Robert H. Goddard, who is generally acknowledged as the father of modern rocketry.

Dr. Goddard started theoretical work on rocket propulsion as early as 1915, in order to study the upper atmosphere and the region beyond. He built and ground-tested a number of small rockets powered by liquid fuel and made his first successful rocket launching on March 16, 1926. This was the actual start of the development of space "hardware."

Shortly after Dr. Goddard's initial success, Germany and Russia became interested in rocket development. By the mid-1930's, scientists in all three countries were firing rockets more than a mile into the air. According to one report, in 1936 the Russians reached an altitude of twelve miles.

At this point, however, the Russians apparently lost interest in rocketry and dropped their developmental program until after World War II. In the United States, Dr. Goddard was unable to find the financial support he needed to build the larger rockets he had planned. It remained for Germany, aware of the military potential of the rocket, to carry forth its development. Throughout World War II, the Germans conducted extensive rocket research at the experimental station of Peenemünde. The research culminated in the development of the huge, deadly V-2 rocket, used against England in the closing months of the war.

The V-2 served as the forerunner of our modern space boosters. After the defeat of Germany, both the United States and the Soviet Union took quantities of V-2's and used them as a basis for developing long-range missiles, which in turn became boosters for early space launchings. Modified versions of the V-2 were also used in the United States to boost instru-

New sight among the stars—the flash of sunlight off tumbling body of a satellite's carrier rocket.

mented packages more than a hundred miles above the Earth in research programs aimed at exploring the upper atmosphere. Although they did not go into orbit, these "sounding" rockets might be considered the first spacecraft.

But these rockets were able to record upper-atmosphere data for only a few minutes. The next logical step was to attempt to put a vehicle into orbit around the Earth, so that it could send back continuous information on air densities, solar radiations, magnetic fields, and other conditions in space.

Early Satellites

On July 29, 1955, the United States announced plans to develop such an orbiting vehicle under a program called Project Vanguard. On October 4, 1957, months before Vanguard was ready for launching, scientists of the U.S.S.R. sent *Sputnik* I into orbit, followed in thirty days by *Sputnik* II. A second American program, called Explorer, resulted in the successful launching of the first U. S. satellite on January 31, 1958. Almost thirty-two years to the day from the time of Dr. Goddard's first launching, *Vanguard* was placed in orbit on March 17, 1958. It is still circling the Earth and transmitting information. Estimates of its orbiting life vary — from 200 to 2,000 years!

Since *Sputnik* I was boosted into orbit, the space-exploration programs of both the United States and the Soviet Union have yielded exceptional results. One of the most spectacular accomplishments of the early years of the Space Age came on April 12, 1961, when the Soviet spacecraft *Vostok* carried cosmonaut Yuri Gagarin through a single orbit and returned him safely to Earth. A month later, the first U.S. manned spacecraft, a bell-shaped capsule named *Freedom* 7, carried astronaut Alan Shepard more than a hundred miles from Earth. On August 6, 1961, the Soviet spacecraft *Vostok* II carried cosmonaut Gherman S. Titov through seventeen orbits.

On February 20, 1962, a giant Atlas rocket lifted American astronaut, Lt. Col. John H. Glenn, into a three-orbit mission.

US ARMY

First U.S. satellite, **Explorer** I, was put in orbit by Jupiter-C rocket. Launch was from Cape Canaveral, January 31, 1958.

Unlike the Soviet cosmonauts, Colonel Glenn was not just a passenger. At times, he actually piloted his capsule, *Friendship 7*, in space. There were 67 systems for him to use or check. Sensors attached to Colonel Glenn's body radioed information about his reactions and physical condition to Earth. Radio signals also carried data about the condition of the spacecraft.

Colonel Glenn — both experiment and experimenter — proved the superiority of man over machine in space. According to one NASA scientist, the flight showed man was "a heck of a lot better than a black box of electronic equipment."

In the four and one-half years of space exploration between *Sputnik* I and *Friendship* 7, the most notable achievements were these:

Four spacecraft escaped Earth's gravity and went into orbit around the sun, where they will remain for millions of years. One of them, the U.S. *Pioneer* V, transmitted data on the interplanetary environment by radio, more than 22,500,000 miles to Earth.

One Soviet spacecraft crashed on the moon on September 13, 1959.

On August 10, 1960, a U.S. spacecraft became the first object ever recovered from Earth orbit.

The first animals to survive Earth orbit were recovered on August 20, 1960, in a Soviet experiment.

As fascinating as are these achievements of the early years, they are only small steps compared with what is to come. Those of us who are alive in these latter years of the twentieth century will witness the greatest adventures of all time, as man moves farther and farther into space. In the following chapters, you will learn about the vehicles man will use to explore the void beyond our atmosphere, the spacecraft which will help us learn the secrets of the mysterious universe.

Types

of

Spacecraft

THERE are a number of types of spacecraft. They differ in size, kinds of instruments, and manner of performance. Each type and its instruments are designed to accomplish certain specific tasks.

The Sounding Rocket

The simplest type of spacecraft is the sounding rocket, which carries a package of instruments to record data. Sounding rockets do not have sufficient velocity to go into orbit. When they have exhausted their rocket power, sounding rockets fall back to Earth. They are a simple, relatively inexpensive method of collecting scientific information, and are used in experiments requiring only a brief exposure to space.

In some cases, the entire sounding rocket is the spacecraft. It contains (1) a set of instruments designed to obtain specific information and (2) equipment to transmit the information

CHAPTER 3

back to Earth for later analysis. In other cases, a rocket is used to boost a payload into space. The payload is usually a capsule containing instruments, cameras, and other devices with which to conduct an experiment. This capsule can be separated or ejected from the main rocket to return to Earth by parachute.

Generally, the sounding rockets in use carry small payloads weighing up to 150 pounds. Most of the sounding rockets fired to date have been launched to altitudes of less than 200 miles. However, sounding rockets may go as high as 4,000 miles. Beyond that altitude, they are no longer considered sounding rockets but "geospace probes."

The Earth Satellite

The type of spacecraft we hear about most often is the Earth satellite. This type of craft moves in an orbit around Earth.

In the past few years, the word "orbit" has become very familiar; but for a better understanding of the operation of an Earth satellite we should take a closer look at this word. The dictionary defines the noun "orbit" as "The path in space along which a heavenly body moves about its center of attraction." Orbit is also used as a verb, meaning, to move along a path centered on some body in space.

Our planet Earth is itself in orbit. Its "center of attraction" is the star we call the sun, and there are eight other planets orbiting around the sun. At this very moment, Earth is hurtling through space at the rate of almost twenty miles per second in its path around the sun; at that rate, it takes approximately 365 days to complete a revolution around the sun.

What keeps the Earth moving in a near-circular path around the sun? It is the sun's gravity, the force which pulls the Earth toward the sun.

The Earth is always falling toward the sun. Why doesn't the Earth fall into the sun? Some basic laws of physics give us the answer. The Earth is a moving body, and like any other

FOUR BASIC SPACECRAFT MISSIONS

VERTICAL PROBE
(sounding rocket)

MANNED SATELLITE

SATELLITE

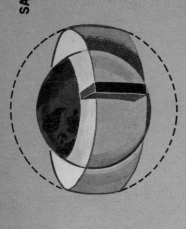

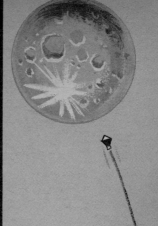

SPACE PROBE

moving body the Earth tends to continue its motion in a straight line. Thus the Earth would move off into space if there were no solar gravity. Since the sun pulls on the Earth with a constant force, the path followed by the Earth becomes nearly circular — the result of two interacting forces.

Earth has a gravitational force of its own and it also has a natural satellite, the moon. The same interacting forces which keep the Earth in orbit about the sun also keep the moon in orbit around the Earth.

Man-made "Moon"

A satellite orbiting around the Earth is a man-made "moon." Its orbit is determined by the same laws that determine the orbits of Earth and the moon.

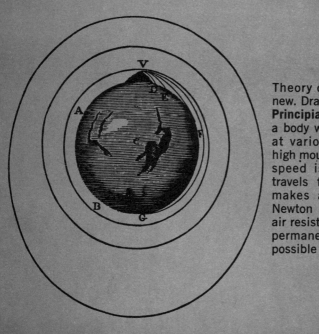

Theory of satellites is not new. Drawing from Newton's **Principia** (1687) shows paths a body would follow if shot at various speeds from a high mountain. As horizontal speed is increased, body travels farther, and finally makes a complete orbit. Newton was also aware of air resistance and knew that permanent satellites were possible only in outer orbits.

In order for a satellite to go into orbit and remain in orbit, it must be provided with a very high speed. Gravity and the curvature of Earth's surface have a fundamental relationship to the orbital velocity of a satellite.

Imagine a satellite that has been lifted by rockets to an altitude of 200 miles, ready to be injected into orbit. The final stage fires, and the satellite is shot horizontally at a speed of five miles per second. Now remember, as it travels horizontally the satellite is also pulled toward the Earth by gravity. And, like any freely falling body near the surface of the Earth, the satellite will drop 16 feet in the first second of its flight. So, as it travels five miles from its point of injection, it falls toward the Earth 16 feet in a curving path. But in five miles, Earth's surface curves away from the horizontal by 16 feet, the distance that the satellite falls.

Thus, after the first second, the satellite is no closer to Earth than it was when it began its horizontal flight. This same series of events takes place each second of the satellite's flight. In short, it always falls toward the Earth but never reaches it.

That is why five miles per second, (18,000 m.p.h.) is the critical speed for injecting a satellite into an orbit close to the Earth. Farther from the Earth, the speed necessary for orbit is lower, because gravitational force between any two objects is inversely proportional to the square of the distance between them. For example, the moon—240,000 miles from Earth—has an orbital speed of 0.6 miles per second.

The first requirement for an orbiting satellite, then, is speed. This speed is provided by a "booster," a high-powered rocket which carries the satellite up to its orbital altitude, gradually accelerating until it reaches the required speed. The second requirement is a method of guidance. The satellite must be aimed into the desired orbital path around Earth. We will discuss boosters and guidance in the following chapter.

Let us assume that the satellite has been "injected" into a precise circular orbit around Earth at a speed of 18,000 miles

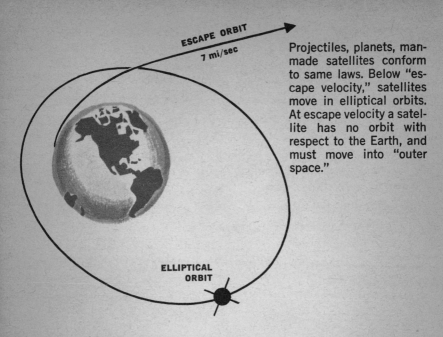

ESCAPE ORBIT
7 mi/sec

Projectiles, planets, man-made satellites conform to same laws. Below "escape velocity," satellites move in elliptical orbits. At escape velocity a satellite has no orbit with respect to the Earth, and must move into "outer space."

ELLIPTICAL ORBIT

ADAPTED FROM PHYSICS IN THE SPACE AGE, BY SCHULZ AND LAGEMANN, LIPPINCOTT, 1961

per hour. In effect, gravity has been offset by the satellite's speed. It seems to be weightless and "floats" in space. But it is floating at the same terrific speed with which it entered orbit. It needs no additional power to maintain its speed, because there is nothing to slow it down. An airplane flying a few miles from the Earth's surface needs constant power to overcome the resistance of the air. In space there is no air to provide resistance, so the satellite continues at its original speed. (Actually, air molecules exist far into space, but in such minute quantities that we can disregard them for purposes of this discussion, since their effect on satellite operation is negligible.)

What if we wanted to bring the satellite back to Earth after a period in orbit? Satellites can be designed to be brought back. They can be fitted with small rockets which are ignited by a radio signal from Earth. These rockets are called "retro rockets." They fire in reverse direction to slow the satellite down. As the satellite slows, its horizontal velocity can no longer offset the Earthward pull of gravity. Gravity takes over and draws the satellite back toward Earth. Still circling, the satellite falls lower and lower on each revolution until it enters the layer of atmosphere surrounding Earth, where air resistance slows it still more.

Although the satellite has slowed considerably, it is still moving at a very high rate of speed, thousands of miles per hour. As it hurtles into the thicker layer of atmosphere at this great speed, the friction of the air particles moving over its surface builds up an intense heat. The temperature rises higher than that of a blast furnace. How can we prevent the satellite from melting under this intense heat?

There are a number of ways to approach this problem of re-entry heating. One method is to build into the satellite a "heat shield," a layer of heavy material which absorbs the friction heat as the satellite plunges through the atmosphere and delays the build-up of temperature on the satellite itself. Protection must be provided if the satellite is to carry humans. In the majority of cases, however, there is no need to bring the satellite back to Earth intact, and it is permitted to burn up in the atmosphere.

All Shapes and Sizes

What does a satellite look like? Actually, there is no single answer. Among the satellites launched to date, some have been spherical, some cylindrical, some bell-shaped. Since the satellite does not have to combat air resistance as it courses through space, the design is flexible. The shape of an airplane is dictated largely by the fact that it must move through the atmosphere. It must have wings, over which the air flows to provide lift, and it must have "streamlining" to minimize the effect of air resistance. But this is not the case with the satellite. It needs no wings or streamlining. It is simply a shell to encase the equipment which is to be sent into space. The type, amount, and size of the equipment determine the shape of the satellite.

A paramount factor in satellite design is weight. In order to go into orbit, the satellite must be boosted to a speed of approximately 18,000 miles per hour. The heavier the satellite, the greater the amount of rocket thrust needed to reach this speed. Because there are limits as to the amount of rocket power presently available, there are also limits as to how heavy a satellite may be.

The path of a satellite around the Earth is more likely to be elliptical than circular. With very precise guidance and speed control, it is possible to place a spacecraft in a circular orbit. But even the slightest deviation in the velocity or in the angle at which the spacecraft is injected into orbit will produce an ellipse. In addition, Earth satellites are usually placed in elliptical orbit deliberately to cover a range of altitudes and hence obtain varied data.

A spacecraft is normally injected into orbit close to Earth, at an altitude of a few hundred miles, but in following its orbit it may reach a point several thousand miles from Earth. The point in orbit closest to the Earth is called the "perigee"; the most distant point is called the "apogee."

Lunar, Planetary, and Interplanetary Spacecraft

In addition to sounding rockets and Earth satellites, a third category of spacecraft includes lunar, planetary, and interplanetary spacecraft. A planetary spacecraft is one designed to explore a specific planet, either by landing on it or orbiting around it. Spacecraft of this type will have aerodynamic design features to help them penetrate the atmosphere of the target planet, if the assigned mission calls for a planetary landing. Interplanetary spacecraft are those which acquire information from the areas between the orbits of the planets. Like the Earth satellites, they need no streamlining or lift devices unless their missions require a return to Earth. Lunar spacecraft, of course, are planned for trips to or near the moon.

These three types of spacecraft have a requirement beyond that of the Earth satellite. Where the Earth satellite remains in a state of balance between Earth's gravity and its own horizontal speed, these farther-traveling craft must completely escape from the pull of Earth's gravity in order to move farther into space.

Escape from Earth

Let's consider an experiment with a weight spinning on the end of the string. At a certain rotational speed, imparted by your hand, the weight stays in a precise circular orbit. Now, suppose you could continue to increase the rotational speed by moving your hand ever faster. What would happen? Eventually, the weight would reach a speed at which the string could no longer hold it. The string would break and the weight would go hurtling off into space.

This illustrates the technique of launching probes to the moon or to the planets. They must escape Earth's gravity, and this is accomplished by providing them with more speed. At a speed of seven miles a second, or about 25,000 miles per hour, the force developed is greater than the opposing pull of gravity. So Earth's gravity becomes the broken string in our illustration and the probe moves off into space.

The path of a planetary or interplanetary spacecraft is an ellipse around the sun. For a better understanding of this path, draw this rough picture of the solar system: Make a point on a piece of paper. This represents the sun. Using the point as the center, draw nine concentric circles. Each circle represents the orbit of one of the planets as it travels around the sun. The third circle is the orbit of Earth, the starting point for all spacecraft. Now draw a curved line from the Earth circle to the fourth circle, which represents the orbit of Mars.

To reach an outer planet such as Mars, space probe is launched in same direction as Earth's orbital motion. Result: an independent velocity greater than Earth's, and probe takes up larger orbit at greater distance from sun. With proper launch velocity and guidance, probe can reach Mars or other planets (see table on facing page). When probe is fired in direction opposite to Earth's orbital motion, it assumes independent velocity less than Earth's and falls into orbit closer to sun. With guidance, it can reach Venus or Mercury.

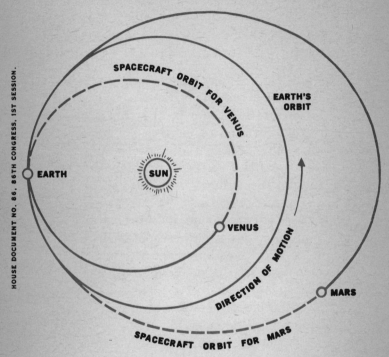

HOUSE DOCUMENT NO. 86, 86TH CONGRESS, 1ST SESSION.

This is the path of the spacecraft, and, of course, the length of the curved line depends on where the planet Mars lies in relation to the Earth. At times Mars is close to Earth; at other times it is on the opposite side of the sun. Curiously, the most favorable time for a Mars launch is not when Mars is nearest Earth, but when it is on the opposite side of the sun. The best Earth-to-Mars path, then, is a half ellipse around the sun which meets Mars' orbit when the sun is between Earth and Mars.

Now draw a curved line out to the ninth circle, the orbit of Pluto. You can see that, because of the distance, the spacecraft would need a much higher initial speed to travel to Pluto than to Mars.

A spacecraft can escape from Earth's gravity at a speed of 25,000 miles per hour, but that speed is not sufficient to take it to Mars. For the Mars mission, a speed of more than 26,000 miles per hour would be required. A trip to Jupiter would require an initial velocity of more than 31,000 miles per hour, and the voyage to distant Pluto would require a speed of about 36,000 miles per hour.

Keeping these factors in mind, we will now move on to a discussion of how the initial velocity is obtained through the use of the launch vehicle.

HOUSE DOCUMENT NO. 86, 86TH CONGRESS, 1ST SESSION.

PLANET	Minimum launching velocity (miles per hour)	Transit time
MERCURY	29,000	110 days
VENUS	26,000	150 days
MARS	26,000	260 days
JUPITER	31,000	2.7 years
SATURN	33,000	6 years
URANUS	35,000	16 years
NEPTUNE	35,000	31 years
PLUTO	36,000	46 years

MINIMUM LAUNCH VELOCITIES TO PLANETS

The
Launch
Vehicle

A SPACECRAFT can be defined as a vehicle that performs an experiment in space. To perform its experiment, it must first be thrust into space through the layer of atmosphere surrounding the Earth. This is the job of the *launch vehicle*.

The launch vehicle resembles a guided missile, and, in fact, most of the early launch vehicles actually were guided missiles. There are now — in being or in development — a number of more advanced launch vehicles especially designed for boosting payloads into space.

Launch vehicles differ considerably in size and in payload-boosting capability, but in general all launch vehicles have three major elements. These are an airframe, a power plant, including a method of propulsion and a supply of propellants, and a system of guidance.

The airframe is simply the structure that encases the other major components of the vehicle, protecting them from damage, either on the ground or in flight.

CHAPTER 4

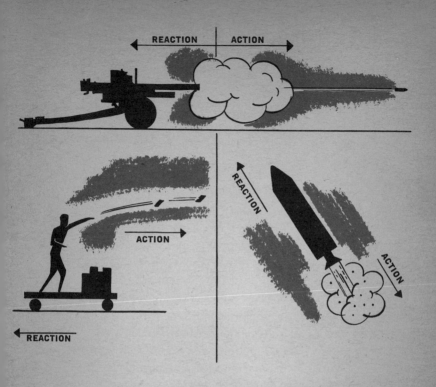

Newton's Third Law: For every action, there is an equal and opposite reaction. Firing a projectile, or throwing bricks off a wagon, causes cannon or wagon to recoil. Rocket recoils from escaping gases.

The Power Plant

Since the rocket engine can operate outside the atmosphere, it is the method of propulsion used for launch vehicles. In simplest terms, a rocket engine is a furnace in which fuel is burned to create a gas. The burning process causes the gas to expand and exert pressure against the outlet provided by the exhaust nozzle of the rocket, through which the gases escape at high speed.

31

It is this high-speed outrushing of the gas stream which provides the power to move the launch vehicle. The source of momentum is expressed by Sir Isaac Newton's Third Law of Motion, which states that for every *action* there is an equal and opposite *reaction*. The rapid movement of the gas through the exhaust nozzle is the *action*. As the gas escapes, it creates a *reaction*, or a push in the opposite direction. More specifically, at the start of a space launch, the gas escapes *downward* creating an *upward* push.

The magnitude of the force created by the *reaction* depends on how much substance is burned and expanded (mass), and how rapidly it passes through the exhaust nozzle (velocity). The force is measured in *pounds of thrust*. To boost a spacecraft into orbit requires a thrust of about one and one-half times the total weight of the launch vehicle and the spacecraft. For instance, if the launch vehicle — including the weight of the rocket engines, their propellants and tankage, the guidance system, the structure of the airframe, and the spacecraft itself — weighs 100,000 pounds, it would take about 150,000 pounds of thrust to place the spacecraft in orbit. Since the huge launch vehicles are extremely heavy, it can readily be seen that tremendous amounts of rocket thrust are required to send even a moderate-size spacecraft beyond the atmosphere.

By far the greatest portion of weight and volume of the launch vehicle is taken up by the rocket propellants. The standard type of rocket power plant is the chemical rocket, which uses two different types of propellants called "fuel" and "oxidizer." In an automobile, power is obtained by burning a mixture of gasoline and oxygen, the latter being extracted from the air. The rocket engine operates on a similar principle, except that it does not draw in oxygen from the atmosphere. However, oxygen or a substitute is required for the burning process. Thus the launch vehicle must carry along a supply of oxidizer which is mixed with the fuel for combustion.

A rocket may use either liquid or solid propellants. Practically all of the rockets launched in space programs to date have been liquid-propelled. From the time of Dr. Goddard's experiments, greatest emphasis has been placed on developing this type of power plant, and the first generation of guided missiles used liquid propellants exclusively. In the liquid-fuel rocket, the fuel and oxidizer are stored in separate tanks within the airframe and fed into a combustion chamber. There they are ignited, creating the propulsive gas which escapes at high velocity to provide thrust. Typical fuels include kerosene, alcohol, and liquid hydrogen. Oxidizers in use include liquid oxygen, nitric acid, and nitrogen tetroxide.

In a solid-fuel rocket, the fuel and oxidizer are contained in a single solid mass. The solid propellant is stored within the rocket combustion chamber, where it is ignited to produce the propulsive gas. The advantages of the solid-fuel rocket are these: it is simpler to handle, because there is no need for the complicated system of tanks, pumps, and valves used in the liquid-fuel rocket. Also the solid-

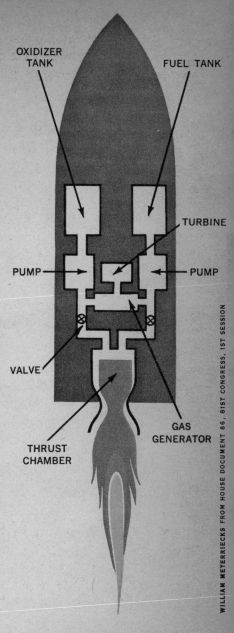

OXIDIZER TANK

FUEL TANK

TURBINE

PUMP

PUMP

VALVE

THRUST CHAMBER

GAS GENERATOR

WILLIAM MEYERRIECKS FROM HOUSE DOCUMENT 86, 81ST CONGRESS, 1ST SESSION

Diagram of liquid-fueled rocket.

fuel rocket can be fueled well in advance of a launch, because the solid fuel can be stored safely for long periods, whereas a liquid oxidizer tends to evaporate rapidly.

Certain combinations of fuel and oxidizer, whether liquid or solid, perform better than others; that is, they develop more thrust per given weight of propellant. Propellant performance is measured by the number of pounds of thrust produced by each pound of propellant in a single second. This is called the "specific impulse" and it is listed in seconds. For instance, when scientists say a typical fuel-oxidizer combination has a specific impulse of 250 seconds, that means it produces 250 pounds of thrust for each pound of propellant burned in one second. Specific impulse is a very important factor in space research. As propellants with higher specific impulses are developed it becomes possible to send larger payloads into space and to accelerate them to higher velocities. For this reason, there is a great deal of propellant research under way on both liquid- and solid-fuel rockets.

Nuclear-fueled Rockets

In addition to the chemical-fueled rocket now used as a power plant for the launch vehicle, there is the nuclear-fueled rocket, still in an early stage of development. In this type of engine, there is no burning process such as that described for the chemical rocket. Instead of the fuel plus oxidizer, a single "working fluid" (liquid hydrogen is the propellant considered most likely) is stored in a tank within the airframe. This fluid is passed through a nuclear reactor which heats it to very high temperatures, creating the exhaust gas which provides thrust. Nuclear-fueled rockets, when fully developed, will yield very high specific impulses. For instance, where current chemical-fueled rockets have specific impulses of from 200 to 300 seconds, it is estimated that the nuclear-fueled rocket will produce a specific impulse of 1,200 seconds. This will enable us to accomplish more advanced space missions, such as sending large payloads to the other planets.

The Guidance System

The final major component of the launch vehicle is the system of guiding and controlling the vehicle to a predetermined point in space. There the payload, or spacecraft, is released from the launch vehicle to go into orbit around the Earth, to probe space and return to Earth, or to escape from Earth's gravity and start a course to another planet.

There are a number of types of guidance systems. The choice of guidance system depends on the mission assigned to

NUCLEAR ROCKET COMPONENTS

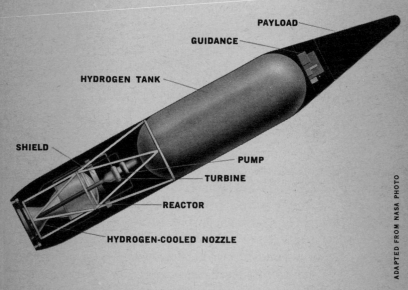

PAYLOAD

GUIDANCE

HYDROGEN TANK

SHIELD

PUMP

TURBINE

REACTOR

HYDROGEN-COOLED NOZZLE

ADAPTED FROM NASA PHOTO

A nuclear rocket promises high specific impulse (pounds of thrust per pound of fuel per second). Instead of burning, fuel vaporizes and expands as reactor heats it, escapes through nozzle to provide thrust.

35

the spacecraft. A sounding rocket, for instance, might be hurled to an altitude of 1,000 miles to perform an experiment and then fall back into the atmosphere. The guidance requirement would be minimal; the rocket need be aimed only toward a planned recovery area, so that it could be retrieved after its brief journey into space.

To place a spacecraft in Earth orbit, however, requires much more precise aiming. At the point of injection into orbit—the point at which the spacecraft usually separates from the launch vehicle—the spacecraft must be in the right position and must be moving at the proper velocity for the desired orbit.

A launch vehicle carrying an Earth satellite is guided only to the point of injection. There are two basic guidance systems which lend themselves to space launches: *inertial guidance* and *radar guidance*.

"Brains" for Guidance

In the most simplified terms, the inertial guidance system has an electronic "brain" which is programed to "know" where the launch vehicle *should* be at all times en route to the point of injection. Another set of instruments measures the side-to-side and fore-and-aft movements of the launch vehicle in flight. This information is relayed to the electronic brain or computer, which continuously computes the speed of the vehicle, its course, and the distance traveled. The brain compares the actual position of the vehicle with the position it "knows" the vehicle should maintain. If the vehicle is off its proper course, the brain actuates controls which correct the course. Course corrections are made by rockets. The launch vehicle may have small auxiliary rockets for this purpose, or the main rocket engine may be caused to swivel. Sometimes the main rocket may have vanes within the exhaust nozzle which can be moved to deflect the flow of gas and thus change the direction of the rocket's course.

The brain also "knows" the exact distance from launch

point to the point of injection, and throughout the flight it measures how far the vehicle has moved along that path. At the precise point of injection, it shuts off the power in the launch vehicle and sets off the mechanism which separates the spacecraft from its carrier. In a liquid-fuel rocket, the brain "orders" the propellant valves to shut, cutting off power immediately. In a solid-fuel rocket, the brain may direct the opening of vents in the walls of the rocket. This causes the pressure to drop and thus extinguishes the flame.

In the radar method of guidance, the launch vehicle carries a radar beacon which continuously sends signals to the ground telling its position. The brain in this case is a computer on the ground. The ground computer compares the actual position of the launch vehicle with the planned position, and sends radio impulses to the vehicle's rockets to correct the position if the vehicle is off course.

Mid-Course Guidance

The inertial and radar systems are called "initial" guidance systems, because they operate only to the point of injection. If the spacecraft is on a planetary mission, it will need further control en route to its destination. This is called "mid-course" guidance. For security reasons, some of the advanced methods of mid-course guidance cannot be discussed, but one important method is a system of automatic celestial navigation. This involves "shooting the stars" to determine position, in the manner that a ship's captain navigates on the high seas. With very precise initial guidance, it is theoretically possible for a spacecraft to land, say, on Mars or Venus without mid-course guidance, but even the slightest error in position or velocity would cause a wide miss. For example, if the speed of the launch vehicle at the point of injection was off by only *one foot per second*, the spacecraft would miss Venus by 25,000 miles. And one foot per second is a very tiny error when you consider that escape from Earth to Venus requires a speed of *38,000 feet per second*.

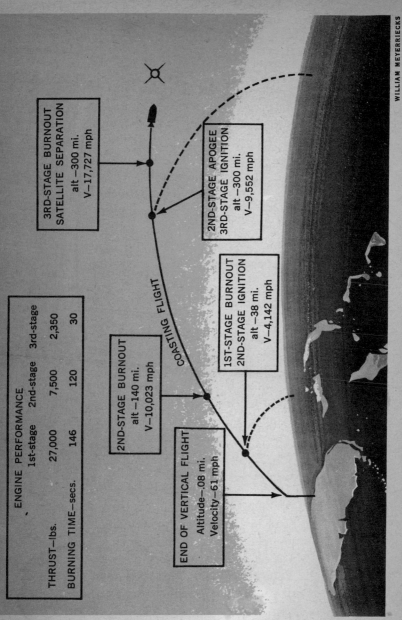

ENGINE PERFORMANCE

	1st-stage	2nd-stage	3rd-stage
THRUST—lbs.	27,000	7,500	2,350
BURNING TIME—secs.	146	120	30

3RD-STAGE BURNOUT
SATELLITE SEPARATION
alt —300 mi.
V—17,727 mph

2ND-STAGE APOGEE
3RD-STAGE IGNITION
alt —300 mi.
V—9,552 mph

1ST-STAGE BURNOUT
2ND-STAGE IGNITION
alt —38 mi.
V—4,142 mph

2ND-STAGE BURNOUT
alt —140 mi.
V—10,023 mph

END OF VERTICAL FLIGHT
Altitude—.08 mi.
Velocity—61 mph

COASTING FLIGHT

WILLIAM MEYERRIECKS

During a three-stage launch, booster stages coast upward, carrying satellite until next firing stage.

38

The Launch Vehicle in Operation

To summarize the operation of the launch vehicle, let us review what happens when a spacecraft is successfully placed in an orbit around the Earth at an altitude of one hundred miles.

At "lift-off," the start of the flight, the launch vehicle at first moves "straight up," but gradually swings into a curved or parabolic flight path toward the point of injection. The gas escaping at high velocity from the rocket's exhaust nozzle provides the thrust, which accelerates the launch vehicle, moving it faster and faster along its path toward the point of injection. Meanwhile, the guidance system is constantly checking the position of the vehicle against the preplanned position, changing course when necessary by applying rocket thrust in the desired direction.

Suppose that the point of injection is planned for an altitude of one hundred miles. As it approaches the hundred-mile level, the launch vehicle is moving at close to 18,000 miles per hour. Acting according to its program, the brain "decides" the vehicle has reached the proper altitude and the proper speed. It shuts off the rocket power and actuates the mechanism which separates the spacecraft from the launch vehicle. This separation can be accomplished in a number of ways. In the method most often employed to date, small explosive charges shear the connecting bolts that hold spacecraft and launch vehicle together and a series of springs push the spacecraft free. The spacecraft — now above the atmosphere which could slow it down, and with Earth's gravity counterbalanced — continues in orbit around the Earth. Depending on its own speed at the point of separation, the launch vehicle may either follow the spacecraft into orbit or it may fall back toward Earth to burn up in the atmosphere.

Rocket Stages

So far, we have discussed the launch vehicle as a single rocket. In practice, it is customary to use more than one rocket or *stage*. Since very high velocities are required for space flight, one rocket may not be able to boost the launch vehicle to required speed, so *multistage* vehicles are employed. In a two-stage rocket, for instance, one rocket is mounted atop another, piggyback fashion. The first rocket fires for perhaps a minute, accelerating the entire vehicle to 10,000 feet per second. Having exhausted its fuel, it separates and falls back to Earth. The second rocket, ignited automatically, takes over and boosts the remaining portion of the vehicle an additional 10,000 feet per second. Since the vehicle started out at 10,000 feet per second, the net velocity is 20,000 feet per second. For greater speeds, more stages can be added.

There is, however, a practical limit to the number of stages that can be employed in one launch vehicle. Remember, each stage has an airframe, structure, and fuel tanks. These add up to a lot of weight. If too many stages were added, the first rocket would not have sufficient power to lift the total weight. A happy compromise is reached by making the upper stages progressively smaller and lighter. Then the basic rocket starts the vehicle moving and each successive stage makes its contribution to the over-all speed. The big advantage is in weight loss en route to space. As each rocket stage exhausts its fuel, it drops off, thus reducing the total weight of the launch vehicle and making the job easier for the succeeding rockets. Most launch vehicles have two, three, or four stages. In one space launch made in April, 1961, a seven-stage vehicle was employed!

Thrust can also be increased by using more than one rocket engine per stage, a technique called "clustering." If one rocket engine can deliver 50,000 pounds of thrust, three engines of the same type can deliver 150,000 pounds. The drawback, of course, is the need for additional tanks and propellants. These increase the weight of the launch vehicle, and in turn increase the amount of thrust required to boost it to the desired speed. Here again space-vehicle designers make the compromise between weight and thrust, selecting the combination of rocket engines and propellant weight which will produce maximum results in terms of launch-vehicle speed and payload. They may learn that for some space missions a single rocket engine is most efficient, while for other missions as many as eight engines may be clustered for greatest efficiency.

The launch vehicle is the carrier which thrusts the spacecraft into space. Next, we will see how the spacecraft accomplishes the mission for which it was designed — providing information to unlock the mysteries of the universe.

Spacecraft

The moment of lift-off! A **Juno II**, its body frosted because of cold liquid oxygen in its tanks, rises to place a 90-pound ionosphere direct measuring satellite, **Explorer** VIII, into orbit. Predawn launch was made November 3, 1960.

at Work

ANY spacecraft has a purpose. It is not merely a scientist's toy, to be hurled into space for the sheer joy of proving it can be done. To send any object into space, manned or unmanned, requires large expenditures of time, effort, and money; and these expenditures would not be sanctioned if we didn't hope to derive some concrete benefits from the experiment.

The basic benefit, we have said, is knowledge. The knowledge gained may be used immediately to better man's way of life in some manner.

Spacecraft Categories

Spacecraft may be broken down into two general categories: applied spacecraft and scientific spacecraft.

Applied spacecraft are those in which space technology is put to work to provide immediate improvements in our everyday living. We have already discussed some examples — weather and communications spacecraft, for instance.

Scientific spacecraft are those which seek purely scientific data, which might be of great interest to the scientific com-

CHAPTER 5

munity but which may not be applied immediately to a "better way of life." However, such data may be applicable at some future date in a manner not currently predictable. An example of a scientific spacecraft is an Earth satellite whose assignment is to study the density of the atmosphere.

In between these two general categories, there is a "gray area" embracing spacecraft which fit both categories. One example is a satellite which studies meteorites. This is basically a scientific study, but it is also immediately applicable to problems of manned space flight. For example, a meteorite can puncture the hull of a spacecraft and endanger the lives of the astronauts. Thus, knowledge of the size, speed, and frequency of meteorites in space permits scientists to devise methods of protection against them, so the *scientific* data can be *applied* to the design of spacecraft. In this example, scientific data is applied in the search for additional scientific data.

To understand the function of a spacecraft as a research tool, let us take a close look at how the spacecraft goes about collecting information.

First, let us consider a spacecraft of the sounding-rocket variety, one which simply penetrates space for a brief period and returns to Earth.

Project NERV

In September, 1960, scientists launched a sounding-rocket experiment called NERV (Nuclear Emulsion Recovery Vehicle). Its mission was to study details of the mysterious cosmic radiation which originates in space. This radiation consists of billions of tiny charged particles which form into great radiation "belts" surrounding the Earth. Where the radiation level is intense, these particles can cause illness or even death to an unshielded human being moving through the radiation belts in a spacecraft. The existence of the radiation belts and some general information on their levels of intensity had been discovered by early U.S. Earth satellites.

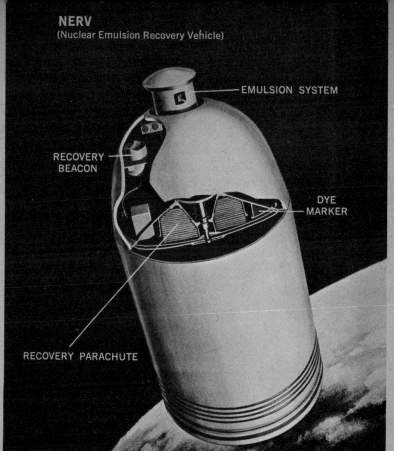

ADAPTED FROM NASA PHOTO

NERV
(Nuclear Emulsion Recovery Vehicle)

EMULSION SYSTEM

RECOVERY
BEACON

DYE
MARKER

RECOVERY PARACHUTE

Cutaway drawing of a NERV capsule, designed to be recovered after a space-probe mission. NERV investigates
cosmic ray activity.

However, scientists wanted more detailed information on
the number of these particles, the amount of charge, how fast
they move, and in what direction. This information is valuable
in determining the amount of shielding necessary for manned
spacecraft.

To get the information, they designed a bell-shaped capsule about sixteen inches long and nineteen inches in diameter,

weighing slightly more than eighty pounds. In it they placed twenty-five sheets of *nuclear emulsion,* a thick photographic film coated with an emulsion sensitive to charged particles. The goal was to take "pictures" of the particles by recording their tracks across the sensitive emulsion. Analysis of the pictures would reveal the desired information about the number of particles, their speed, direction, and amount of charge.

Recording Radiation

The capsule was the spacecraft. Its launch vehicle was a four-stage sounding rocket called Argo D-8. Each of the four stages was propelled by a solid-fuel rocket. The launch vehicle boosted the small NERV capsule to an altitude of 1,260 miles. Then the launch vehicle and capsule together dropped to the top of the atmosphere, where the capsule was ejected. As it passed through the radiation belts on the way up and again on the way down, the spacecraft trapped the charged particles through a porthole in the capsule, and the photographic emulsion made a precise record of the amount of radiation.

The film had to be processed in order to develop the identifying tracks made by the particles — the clues for scientific study. Thus, completion of the experiment required recovery of the spacecraft. The capsule was provided with an automatic parachute, which opened at the proper time to lower the spacecraft to Earth. To assist its recovery, the capsule also had a radio beacon that sent out signals to trackers on the ground as it descended from space. The capsule and its valuable film were recovered and sent to the laboratories for detailed analysis.

NERV is typical of a great many experiments performed by spacecraft of the sounding-rocket type. In these experiments, the spacecraft is not always recovered; sometimes the information is radioed back to Earth during the period of time that the vehicle is in space.

The Earth-orbiting satellite is usually a more complex

spacecraft than the payload of a sounding rocket. Most scientific satellites are designed to perform, not one, but a number of experiments as the spacecraft circles the Earth. Each experiment requires a different instrument or set of instruments, so the number of experiments which can be made depends on the amount of payload which can be sent aloft. This in turn is dependent upon the amount of thrust available in the launching vehicle.

Even some of the smaller satellites, however, are capable of handling several different experiments. American scientists have made considerable progress in "miniaturizing" the data-recording instruments that go into a satellite. In this manner, instruments are made smaller without impairing their reliability. For example, a relatively small satellite called *Explorer* VII weighs only 91.5 pounds. Shaped like two cones joined together at their bases, it is thirty inches in diameter. Yet, within this small space, it contains instruments to carry out seven different experiments, together with other equipment to collect the data and transmit it back to Earth.

Let's examine *Explorer* VII as an illustration of how an Earth satellite performs its assignment.

Explorer VII was boosted into space by a four-stage launch vehicle called *Juno* II. It went into an elliptical orbit with a perigee (point closest to Earth) of 344 miles altitude and an apogee (point most distant from Earth) of 678 miles altitude. It will remain in orbit for about twenty years.

Explorer VII's experiments were concerned primarily with radiation, so before discussing how the satellite acquired information, let us first discuss radiation.

Electromagnetic Radiation

In the vacuum of space, there are many different types of radiation. Generally, they are banded together under the heading "electromagnetic radiation." Light is a form of electromagnetic radiation; as are radiated heat, radio and radar waves,

X rays and gamma rays. What is the difference among them?

Radiation is classified by "wave length," ranging from very long waves to very short waves. The total range is called the electromagnetic spectrum. Take an ordinary twelve-inch ruler and imagine it is the electromagnetic spectrum. At the left-hand side of the ruler are the long-wave radiations. Roughly half of the ruler, or spectrum, is taken up by various types of radio waves — such as the radio used in aircraft or satellites, your standard home radio, television, and radar.

As we progress toward the other end of the ruler, the wave lengths become shorter. After radar comes infrared radiation. Then, at about the seven-inch mark on the ruler, comes visible light. Visible light is a very tiny portion of the total spectrum; if we assume the ruler to be the total spectrum, visible light would occupy only about one sixteenth of an inch. Still moving toward the shorter wave lengths, after visible light we come to ultraviolet rays, X rays, and gamma rays. All of this radiation moves through space at approximately the speed of light, which is now computed to be 186,300 miles per *second*.

Cosmic rays are a different type of radiation, in that they consist of very tiny particles, actually nuclei of some of the lighter elements such as hydrogen.

Only a very small portion of the total electromagnetic spectrum penetrates the layer of atmosphere which surrounds the Earth; visible light does, of course, and so do certain portions of the radio part of the spectrum. When cosmic radiation enters our atmosphere, its character changes; so to study it properly we must study it in space, its native habitat.

Scientists are very much interested in every type of radiation present in space — its amount, its energy, its source, and other details which are tiny parts of the jigsaw puzzle of the universe and its origins. With spacecraft, scientists now have tools with which to explore these phenomena.

Since the experiments in *Explorer* VII were concerned with radiation of one type or another, let's see how the satellite went

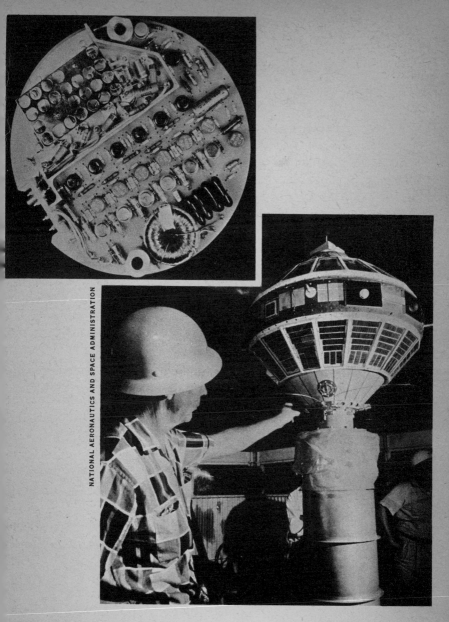

NATIONAL AERONAUTICS AND SPACE ADMINISTRATION

An engineer makes a final inspection of the 91.5-pound **Explorer** VII Earth satellite. Even a very small satellite is complex, as the inset view of Explorer's main electronic chassis indicates.

about collecting the information scientists needed to have.

Experiment Number One was concerned with the thermal radiation balance, or "heat budget" of our Earth. The sun is a gigantic nuclear reactor pouring energy throughout the solar system. Only two billionths of the sun's total energy output reaches Earth. Some of this energy is absorbed as heat; some of it is reflected, or bounced back, into space. The Earth receives the greatest amount of heat from the sun at the Equator, and correspondingly less toward the North and South Poles. However, scientists have determined that at the poles the Earth reflects and radiates more heat than is received there. This means that some of the heat being received at the middle latitudes is being transferred to the poles by the atmosphere and by ocean currents. This transfer of heat has great influence on our weather, and scientists want to know more about it. The questions "asked" of *Explorer* VII were these:

1) How much heat radiation from the sun falls on the "top" of our atmosphere?

2) How much of it is reflected back into space?

3) How much of it is absorbed by the Earth, its clouds, and its atmosphere?

By comparing the respective data, scientists can chart the amount of "heat transfer" on Earth.

Sensing Elements

To measure the various factors, *Explorer* VII was equipped with a number of "sensing elements." The sensors were hemispherical in shape and about the size of half a golf ball. They were located on the outer surface of the satellite, where they would encounter the different types of radiation from the sun and from the Earth. Some were painted black; these were equally sensitive to radiation from the sun and to radiation from the Earth. Others were painted white; these were more sensitive to radiation from Earth than that from the sun. Another, with a polished gold surface, was more sensitive to radiation from the sun than to the radiation "bounced" back from Earth.

Each of the sensors was equipped with a small electric thermometer, and the temperature recorded was an indication of the amount of radiation present. In a very complicated series of calculations comparing the data recorded by each of the sensors, scientists can get the answers to the questions asked of *Explorer* VII.

Measuring the Sun's Radiation

Experiment Number Two was concerned with measuring some of the electromagnetic radiation we just discussed, in this case radiation coming from the sun. Specifically, *Explorer* VII was "asked" to measure X rays and ultraviolet rays, short-wave portions of the spectrum.

The satellite was equipped with two small cylinders, each about the size of a three-inch flashlight battery. The cylinders were filled with special gases that can detect the presence of radiation. One cylinder was designed to measure X rays and the other to measure solar ultraviolet radiation, the invisible light that can cause sunburn. Each cylinder had a window, mounted in the outer shell of the satellite. The radiation entered the window and was trapped by the gas. The amount of radiation present was then measured by the change in the electrical properties of the gas.

Experiment Number Three was a measurement of heavy primary cosmic rays, which are atoms stripped of their electrons so that just the nuclei are left. They are tiny particles rather than rays, with tremendously high amounts of energy. A giant atom smasher, such as is used in scientific work, may have the power of one billion electron volts; but these heavy primary cosmic rays have energies as high as a *billion billion* electron volts. To measure their intensity, another gas-filled cylinder similar to that used for X-ray and ultraviolet radiation was employed.

Experiment Number Four involved measurement of some of the less energetic particles in the great radiation belts around Earth. These particles can be harmful to human life; and since manned spacecraft will have to pass through the radiation zone, measurement of the intensity and energy of these is important. The measurements were made by equipment similar in principle to, but slightly different from, the cylindrical chambers used in Experiment Number Three.

Solar Cells

The performance of the solar cell was the subject of Experiment Number Five in *Explorer* VII. This solar cell was a specially fabricated crystal window coated with silicon, which traps radiation from the sun. All radiation is a form of energy, and this energy can be trapped and put to work. In advanced spacecraft, solar energy may be used to power the spacecraft. In current satellites, it is used to provide power for the radio-sending equipment, which transmits the information back to Earth. The solar cell or window catches radiant energy from the sun and converts it into electrical potential or voltage to power the satellite's radio transmitter.

Most of the surface of *Explorer* VII was covered with these small windows to obtain power. For Experiment Number Five, one cell had special equipment to measure the variations in voltage over a long period. The object was to study the performance of the cell to see how long and how well it functioned in the presence of radiation.

Micrometeorites

Experiment Number Six dealt with micrometeorites which, as their name implies, are very tiny meteors or particles of cosmic dust smaller than grains of sand. Of unknown origin, micrometeorites hurtle through space at speeds from 25,000 to more than 150,000 miles per hour. They are of interest scientifically because of the mystery of their origin. They are also of practical interest, since, traveling at such speeds, they could develop enough momentum to puncture the hull of a manned spacecraft.

In this experiment, scientists "asked" *Explorer* VII to find out how often micrometeorites are encountered in space. Some indication can be obtained by measuring how many times they struck the satellite. The satellite was equipped with three "photoconductors" covered by film shutters of extremely thin aluminum. The photoconductor and shutter work like a camera — a micrometeorite punctures the film shutter, letting in light, and the photoconductor records the impact of the particle.

Experiment Number Seven, the final experiment of *Explorer* VII, was simply a measurement of the temperature on the surface of the satellite. As *Explorer* VII moved in orbit around the Earth, it was sometimes in direct sunlight unfiltered by the atmosphere, at other times it was in cosmic darkness as it moved behind the Earth. Temperatures were measured by electric thermometers. *Explorer* VII reported that satellite temperatures ranged between 32 degrees Fahrenheit, when Earth was between the satellite and the sun, and 140 degrees Fahrenheit when *Explorer* VII was in direct sunlight.

Sending Space Data to Earth

Such were the experiments and the equipment in *Explorer* VII. Now, how did the satellite send the information back to Earth?

It is possible to design unmanned spacecraft which can return to Earth, their instruments and records intact. *Explorer* VII, however, was not one of this type. It will circle the Earth for another two decades, gradually slowing down as it makes contact with the few atmospheric particles which are found in its orbit. When it slows down sufficiently, gravity will take over and the spacecraft will plunge into the heavier atmosphere, where it will burn up as a result of atmospheric friction.

Explorer VII must send its information from space. The system by which this is accomplished is called *telemetry*.

Telemetry is simply radio communication from the spacecraft to a receiving station on Earth. It requires one or more transmitters in the satellite and a source of transmitter power. Telemetry might be compared to a radio broadcast. An announcer talks into a microphone. The microphone converts the sound waves generated by his voice into electrical impulses which are beamed through the air on a certain frequency. By tuning your home radio to that frequency, you pick up these signals, and the receiver in your radio converts the signals back to audible sound.

To describe telemetry from a spacecraft, let us take a specific example, such as the micrometeorite experiment in *Explorer* VII. A micrometeorite punctures the aluminum-covered window on the surface of the spacecraft and the impact is registered. An electrical system "tells" the transmitter of the impact, and the transmitter immediately sends a signal to the receiving station on Earth, which is tuned to the special frequency assigned to *Explorer* VII.

At the station, this signal is recorded on a reel of magnetic tape. Each different type of experiment — cosmic rays, heat balance, temperature, X rays, and so forth — makes a different type of coded mark on the tape. The times at which these marks are made are also recorded on the tape. Later, scientists can take the tapes and decode them. They relate the information received to the known position of the satellite at the time it was recorded, and make the calculations and measurements which produce the desired scientific information. The scientists are aided in this painstaking analysis of the tapes by electronic computers, which handle in seconds the calculations it might take men months to make. Even so, analysis of a taped satellite-data record is a long process, sometimes requiring many months.

To send the signals, the transmitter needs power. In *Ex-*

plorer VII, a combination of batteries and solar cells were employed. The solar cells converted radiant energy from the sun into electric power for the transmitter. However, *Explorer* VII was not always in sunlight; as it passed behind the Earth, it could not pick up solar radiation. So, to permit sending data during this dark period, the transmitter was provided with a pair of storage batteries for power. Alternately, solar energy took over again. The solar cells charged the batteries during the daylight sector of its orbit.

That is the basic system of telemetry used for *Explorer* VII. There are several variations of the system, however. One of the drawbacks of the *Explorer* VII equipment was that the satellite could send information only when it was over or near a receiving station. These stations are located at various points on the Earth's surface, but even so there were times when the satellite was "out of sight" of all stations. Thus, some of the information transmitted was never recorded.

Advanced Telemetry

To overcome this deficiency, a more advanced system was developed. In this system, the spacecraft itself can be equipped with one or more tape recorders. As data from each of the experiments is obtained, it is recorded on tape and stored until the satellite is within range of a receiving station. At that time, operators in the station can "ask" the satellite for all or any specific part of its stored information by sending a radio signal. The tape recorder then plays back its stored information, which is relayed to Earth by the transmitter.

Television is also used in spacecraft-to-Earth communications when a photographic record is desirable, such as a photo of the cloud cover of the Earth. The image recorded by the space camera is converted to electrical impulses, relayed to Earth by the transmitter, and "unscrambled" into a picture at the receiving station.

We have discussed the methods of operation of two types

of spacecraft, the sounding rocket and the Earth satellite. The third type is the space probe, a spacecraft which goes to the vicinity of a specific planet, or moves in an orbit between planets. There have not been many interplanetary probes to date, but one of the most successful and most fascinating was *Pioneer* V.

An Interplanetary Spacecraft in Operation

Pioneer V was designed to orbit around the sun between the orbits of Venus and Earth. To get an idea of the path of the spacecraft, mark a dot on a piece of paper and draw two concentric circles around it. The dot is the sun. The circle closest to the dot is the orbit of Venus. The outer circle is Earth's orbit. Draw an ellipse lying between the two circles and that, roughly, is the path of *Pioneer* V. It is in orbit around the sun, a tiny man-made planet, making one orbit of 514,000,-000 miles every 312 days.

In order to go into solar orbit, *Pioneer* V first had to escape from Earth's gravity. This was accomplished by a powerful three-stage Thor-Able launch vehicle, which boosted the spacecraft to a speed of about 25,000 miles per hour. At this speed, the outward push was greater than the pull of Earth's gravity, so *Pioneer* V left Earth forever. As it escaped Earth, it came under the influence of the sun's gravity, which accelerated the spacecraft to a speed of 78,000 miles per hour. This speed is sufficient to keep *Pioneer* V in solar orbit forever, in the same manner that Earth itself remains in solar orbit.

Pioneer V is a beach-ball-size sphere, twenty-six inches in diameter, weighing ninety-five pounds. From its "equator"— the centerline of the sphere — extend four large paddles. Each of these paddles contains 1,200 solar cells, a total of 4,800 cells which continuously charge fourteen small batteries. The batteries power two transmitters. The telemetry system is of the command type; that is, the spacecraft sends signals in response to command signals from Earth. *Pioneer* V sent back information from a point 22,500,000 miles from Earth, which was an extraordinary accomplishment. Then, since its transmitter did not have sufficient power to send signals over the greater distances involved, it was heard no more.

Pioneer V's Experiments

The equipment aboard *Pioneer* V was designed to make four experiments. The experiments were similar to those in *Explorer* VII and performed in similar manner, but of course the data were different because *Pioneer* V is operating in interplanetary space, millions of miles from Earth, while *Explorer* VII is orbiting close to Earth.

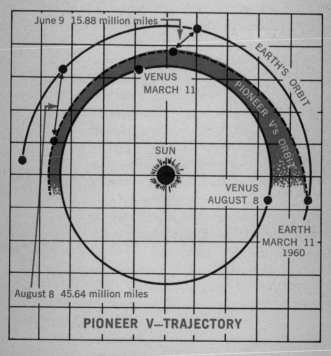

June 9 15.88 million miles

EARTH'S ORBIT

PIONEER V's ORBIT

VENUS MARCH 11

SUN

VENUS AUGUST 8

EARTH MARCH 11 1960

August 8 45.64 million miles

PIONEER V—TRAJECTORY

ADAPTED FROM NASA PHOTO BY WILLIAM MEYERRIECKS

The initial path of interplanetary probe **Pioneer** V between the orbits of Earth and Venus. Radio contact with **Pioneer** V lasted until probe was more than 22,500,000 miles from Earth, setting a record.

Pioneer V had a counter to measure solar radiation. This consisted of seven gas-filled chambers such as those described for *Explorer* VII. It also had two chambers to measure the distribution of cosmic rays in deep space. It had a device called a "magnetometer," which measured the magnetic force in the great magnetic fields surrounding Earth and in interplanetary space. Finally, it had a micrometeorite counter. It is interesting to note that, although *Pioneer* V had moved a million miles into space in the first seven days of its endless journey, it had recorded only eighty-seven micrometeorite hits.

These three spacecraft — NERV, the sounding rocket, *Explorer* VII, the Earth satellite, and *Pioneer* V, the interplanetary probe — are representative of their various classes. However, it must be remembered that they are relatively crude products of the "Stone Age" of space exploration. Already, much more advanced spacecraft are ready for use. Instruments of greater capability, or "sophistication" as scientists term it, are being developed. They will be capable of collecting and transmitting back to Earth a much wider variety of space data. As more powerful launch vehicles become available, the spacecraft will become much larger and will take on different shapes, depending on their assigned missions. Communications systems will be developed to permit receipt of information from greater distances which will make even *Pioneer* V's 22,500,000-mile transmission seem insignificant. Spacecraft will be designed to maneuver in space, to change their speed or orbit, to circle or land on other planets. It is even possible that someday we may send a spacecraft to retrieve *Pioneer* V from its lonely orbit for scientific study.

In later chapters we will discuss these advanced spacecraft. First, however, let us examine the manned spacecraft, what it can do and what new designs and equipment are needed to permit man to survive and operate in the alien environment of space.

Man
in
Space

THE real conquest of space demands that man himself venture out into the void beyond our atmosphere. The automatic instruments in unmanned spacecraft are masterpieces of modern technology, but they are no match for nature's masterpiece, the human brain.

Occasionally, the argument is advanced that instrumented spacecraft can obtain all the desired information about space. Most experts concerned with space exploration will disagree. As sophisticated as the most advanced instruments are, they can only report; they cannot evaluate what they "see." In the quest for scientific knowledge, the best possible combination of research tools is *man* and the instruments.

Finally, there is the philosophical aspect of space exploration. After dreaming for countless centuries of leaving his planet to explore the universe, can man now forego the opportunity presented by modern technology simply because it is expensive and dangerous? It will be expensive, certainly, but the potential result justifies the expense. And danger has

CHAPTER 6

never been a deterrent to pioneers, from Columbus to the Wright brothers.

Man *will* venture farther into space. He has already demonstrated his ability to survive in space if provided with the proper protection. True, the first manned space flights were of relatively brief duration. Nevertheless, they proved that man has already solved at least some of the basic problems of human survival in the alien environment of space. The problem will increase in proportion to the distance man moves from Earth and the time he spends in space. However, clear lines of solution are already evident.

Protection for Man in Space

The manned spacecraft is necessarily a more complex vehicle than its unmanned counterpart. The basic mechanics of thrusting the craft into space are the same. The types of spacecraft—sounding rockets, Earth satellites, and space probes of the lunar, planetary, and interplanetary varieties—are the same. The complexity stems from the efforts to provide protection so that man can exist in a totally unfamiliar and challenging environment.

The best available illustration of what is involved in the construction of a manned spacecraft can be had by examining the systems and equipment in the Project Mercury capsule which took the first U.S. astronauts into space. Compared with tomorrow's spacecraft, the Mercury capsule is a "Model T" of the Space Age, yet it contains the basic systems for human survival and it has proved that they work. The Mercury capsule, shaped like a large bell, is about six feet wide at its bottom and about ten feet long. Although tiny by comparison with spacecraft to come, it is considerably larger than most of the early U.S. satellites and space probe payloads. The Mercury capsule weighs about two tons and the major portion of its weight is taken up by equipment designed to protect its occupant.

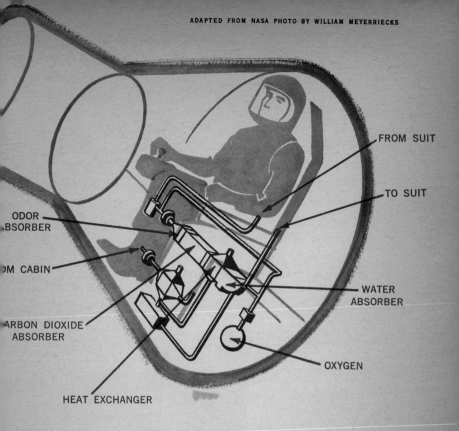

FROM SUIT

TO SUIT

ODOR
ABSORBER

OM CABIN

WATER
ABSORBER

CARBON DIOXIDE
ABSORBER

OXYGEN

HEAT EXCHANGER

A cutaway drawing of the "life support" system used with an astronaut's space suit. It provides him with purified, pressurized air, and can function for up to 28 hours. The space capsule's cabin has still another system.

The cabin is designed, as nearly as possible, to duplicate environmental conditions of the surface of the Earth, to which man is adapted. First, the astronaut must have oxygen to breathe. He must also be provided with an atmospheric pressure close to that of Earth; otherwise at the very low pressures of space his blood would boil. Beneath the couch on which the astronaut lies during flight are two tanks, each containing four pounds of oxygen. A pump forces the oxygen into the cabin, in much the same manner that airliners are "pressurized" so that the passengers can breathe normally at altitudes where outside air is much too thin for normal breathing.

The Mercury Space Suit

To permit the astronaut to perform his functions in comfort, the temperature in the cabin is carefully controlled by a type of air conditioner called a "heat exchanger." Hot air from the cabin is drawn into this heat exchanger by a fan, cooled by water, and directed back into the cabin. This system keeps the Mercury capsule comfortable even during the "hot" period when the capsule re-enters the dense atmosphere and air friction builds up enormously high temperatures on the outside of the capsule.

Besides being protected by the cabin pressure system, the

Finding a heat shield for Project Mercury's

astronaut wears a space suit. This is no ordinary flying suit; it is actually a compact version of the cabin. A hose leads from the oxygen tanks to the waist of the space suit. Should something go wrong with the cabin pressure, an automatic device immediately starts pumping air into the suit to provide breathing air and adequate pressure. The suit also has its own air-conditioning system similar to the one which cools the cabin.

As he breathes, the astronaut exhales carbon dioxide, which can be poisonous if sufficient quantities are allowed to accumulate. Also, he perspires and gives off body odors. The oxygen stream entering the suit picks up the carbon dioxide, water vapor from perspiration, and body odors and exhausts them through an exit hose in the helmet of the suit. They pass through a chemical canister which removes the carbon dioxide and body odors, then through a "water evaporator," a sponge-

psule: a Fiberglas and plastic model takes blast of 5,000°F. air stream.

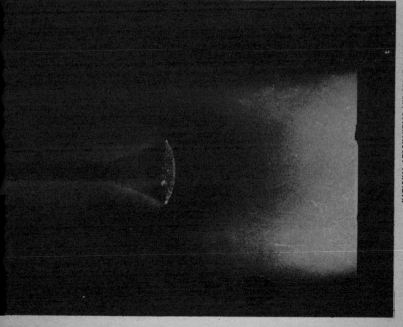

NATIONAL AERONAUTICS AND SPACE ADMINISTRATION

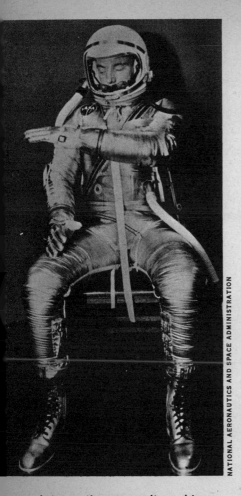

NATIONAL AERONAUTICS AND SPACE ADMINISTRATION

Astronaut's space suit provides an environment approaching that of Earth. He is protected against low pressure, heat. Body reactions can be measured and monitored.

like device that absorbs the water. The purified oxygen stream is directed back into the suit for re-use.

All of these systems work automatically, and each system has a "back-up" system — if one system fails the other automatically starts operating. The astronaut's instrument panel tells him how each part of the system is working. All of this intricate equipment is located under the foam-rubber couch on which the astronaut lies during flights. Despite its complexity, it takes up little more space than the simple system which operates your family refrigerator.

In addition to these protective devices, the capsule also has a two-way radio, permitting conversation between the astronaut and the ground stations. Telemetering equipment transmits data on the astronaut's physical condition to a physician at the ground station. Wires are affixed to various parts of the astronaut's body and connected to the telemetry transmitter. In this way, his heart beat, breathing rate, pulse, body temperature, and other important physiologic details are observed.

To keep the spacecraft from spinning or going end over end, small jets are mounted on the capsule. The astronaut fires these jets by moving a control handle. The jet blast moves the capsule up and down or from side to side. The tiny jets produce only a few pounds of thrust, but that is all that is required in space where there is no air resistance to overcome.

Returning the Manned Spacecraft to Earth

Unlike the unmanned satellite, which can be permitted to burn up in the atmosphere when its usefulness is ended, the manned spacecraft must be brought safely back to Earth. This requires a new set of devices. Here again we will use the Mercury capsule as an illustration.

The first requirement is to slow down the spacecraft to bring it out of orbit. This is accomplished by small "retro rockets," located at the bottom of the capsule (actually the front end as the capsule moves in orbit, because the capsule changes position after launch). When these rockets are fired toward the line of flight, they act like the brakes in an automobile and produce a force opposite to the direction of movement. The retro rockets may be triggered either by the astronaut or by the ground station.

As the retro rockets slow down the capsule, the balance between velocity and gravity is destroyed and the spacecraft drops Earthward. Now comes the critical "re-entry." Although the capsule has lost some of its orbital velocity, it is still moving at a terrific rate — 10,000 to 15,000 miles per hour. At this speed contact between capsule and even very thin air builds up great friction which would destroy the capsule if protection were not provided. The protection is a "heat shield," a heavy layer of Fiberglas on the bottom of the capsule, which strikes the atmosphere first. A part of this shield actually melts from the friction heat. Melting is a change of state requiring large amounts of heat. Thus, the heat energy is absorbed so that it does not spread to the other parts of the capsule.

After re-entry, the capsule slows down more and more from air resistance. When it drops to about 10,000 feet altitude, it still is moving at a few hundred miles per hour — much too fast for a landing impact. To slow the spacecraft further, a large parachute pops from the top of the capsule. To cushion the landing impact even more, there is a large rubber cushion between the heat shield and the cabin. This automatically inflates like a balloon and permits a gentle "touch-down."

Such, in brief, are the major systems in the Project Mercury spacecraft. It is apparent that there are a great many factors to be considered in the design of a manned spacecraft, even a "Model T" spacecraft like the Mercury capsule. Remember, the Mercury system is designed to put only one man in space for a period of not more than twenty-eight hours. The design problems and survival requirements are compounded many times for manned spacecraft capable of performing advanced space missions, such as a landing on the moon or a visit to another planet.

Let us consider some of the design requirements for more advanced manned space missions.

Manned Spacecraft after Mercury

Next step after Mercury is the "multi man" spacecraft, capable of orbiting the Earth as a space laboratory for periods of about fourteen days, or of making a trip around the moon without landing. In this type of spacecraft, all of the protection built into the Mercury capsule must be applied on a larger scale. These spacecraft will have a crew of three, so the cabin will have to have provision for pressurization, breathing oxygen, temperature control, and waste elimination for three men for fourteen days instead of one man for one day. This can be accomplished by "recycling" the various materials, using them over and over. Take oxygen for instance. In the body, inhaled oxygen is converted to carbon dioxide; the exhaled carbon dioxide can be reconverted to oxygen and carbon by a chemical system. The oxygen can then be recycled for breathing.

In order to eliminate the large fleet needed for sea-search and recovery, the Mercury system of landing in the ocean will be scrapped in favor of landing at a preselected site on land. This means that the craft will have to have some form of aerodynamic lift built into its design, together with controls for maneuvering in the atmosphere, like an airplane. The single Mercury landing parachute will not suffice for the heavier multi-man spacecraft. It must have at least two parachutes, or a vertical descent system such as a helicopter's rotor blades.

There must be provision for storing food, which takes up space and weight even in the most condensed form. The spacecraft also must carry equipment for emergency repairs, since the chance of an emergency increases with the duration of the voyage.

Obviously, a major requirement is greatly increased thrust in the launch vehicle, due to the heavier weight of the spacecraft.

Lunar Spacecraft

As we progress to the next step, manned landing on the moon, we encounter a new set of design problems. All of the previous considerations apply, but there are additional requirements.

First, there must be an extremely powerful launch vehicle to start the spacecraft on its trip to the moon. Then, the spacecraft must have an advanced guidance system to reach the moon and maneuver into position for a landing. It must have powerful retro rockets to cushion the landing on the moon.

If the astronauts will venture out of their spacecraft onto the atmosphereless surface of the moon, a very advanced type of space suit will be required. All of the protection provided by the complicated equipment in the spacecraft must be built into the suit itself.

To leave the moon and return to Earth, more rocket power

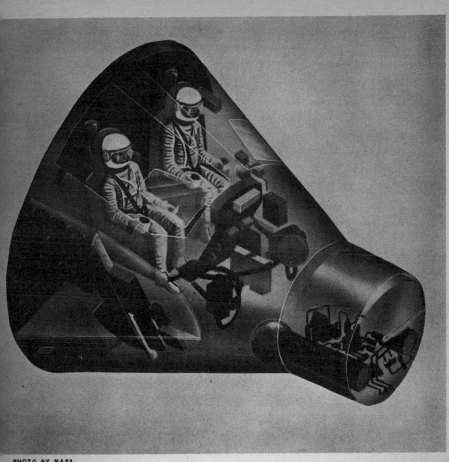

PHOTO BY NASA

Two-man spacecraft for project Gemini will have 50 per cent greater volume than, and weigh two to three times as much as, the one-man spacecraft used in Project Mercury experiments. Gemini spacecraft, to be boosted into orbit by Titan II rockets, will undergo first series of flight tests in 1963-64. Following unmanned flight tests, plans are to place two astronauts in extended Earth-orbit missions lasting from a few days up to a week or more. The two-man capsule will also be used in experiments to develop space-rendezvous docking techniques in which manned spacecraft will join with an Atlas-Agena B rocket motor previously placed in orbit.

is needed. Escape from the moon is easier than escape from Earth, since the moon's gravitational force is only one-sixth as great as Earth's. Nonetheless, to propel a large spacecraft away from the moon, powerful rockets and large quantities of fuel are needed, as well as a very precise guidance system to place the spacecraft in the proper path for a return to Earth. Re-entry into Earth's atmosphere from a moon trip requires greater heat shielding, because of higher re-entry speed.

Interplanetary Spacecraft

When we think of interplanetary travel even to the nearest planets, the problems become enormous. Once again we need pressurization, breathing oxygen, temperature control, waste elimination systems, and recycling systems; but they must function perfectly for much longer periods of time. At escape velocity of 26,000 miles an hour, a round trip to Venus, our nearest neighbor, will take about three months. Almost four months are required for a round trip to Mars, and more than five months for a round trip to Mercury. Thus, every component of the spacecraft must operate reliably for months, and numerous "back-up" systems will be required to take over in the event of failure.

In discussing lunar voyages, we passed lightly over the radiation problem. From data produced by the early spacecraft, scientists are charting radiation space maps which show where the danger areas lie. In Earth-orbiting missions, it will be possible to avoid these radiation belts or to pass quickly through them at the point of their weakest intensity. For lunar or interplanetary missions, however, radiation protection will have to be built into the spacecraft, because of the long duration of the voyage and the probability of encountering a solar storm, during which radiation reaches its highest levels.

Similarly, there must be protection against the possibility of a hull puncture by a meteorite, since long periods in space increase the chance of a strike.

Early manned space flights have indicated that periods of weightlessness are not a problem for short periods. No one yet knows whether weightlessness is a problem when the condition exists for months. It could, for instance, cause astronauts to become disoriented so that they could not perform jobs. It may even cause them to become ill. The interplanetary spacecraft will probably have to have its own artificial gravity to combat this problem. Artificial gravity can be induced by rotating the craft in flight, but this poses still more design problems.

Communications with Earth are very important and they become a problem because of the distances involved. Radio sets have been developed which can operate up to 50,000,000 miles from Earth, but this is a trifling distance if we are ever to explore space in the region of the outer planets. Jupiter, for instance, is about 387,000,000 miles from Earth; Uranus, more than 1.6 billion miles; Neptune and Pluto, more than three billion miles!

These are just some of the basic problem areas connected with the development of manned spacecraft. There are a great many more specific problems. Even the briefest résumé of the areas of difficulty serves to illustrate why manned space exploration will take a long time, a great deal of research and large sums of money.

Nonetheless, manned exploration of the solar system will come, in time. For some of the problems, solutions are already in development; for others, solutions appear possible. In a later chapter, we will discuss advanced space missions and the lines of approach toward solving these problems.

Launch Vehicles
for
Future
Space Missions

THROUGHOUT the early chapters of this book, there has been one recurrent fact: The weight of the spacecraft is limited by the power available in the launch vehicle. To reach space, the spacecraft must be blasted through the layer of atmosphere which rings Earth, fighting the drag of the billions of tiny air molecules which tend to retard the progress of the space vehicle. At the same time, the space vehicle must develop sufficient velocity so that it overpowers the force of Earth's gravity which tends to pull any object toward the center of Earth.

This takes power, or rocket thrust. The amount of thrust required to put a payload in space cannot be stated in a simple equation. It depends upon a number of factors. In every launch — regardless of mission — the weight of the spacecraft and the size and weight of the launch vehicle must be considered. If the spacecraft is an Earth-orbiting vehicle, the desired

CHAPTER 7

NATIONAL AERONAUTICS AND SPACE ADMINISTRATION

altitude of orbit is a factor, as is the distance from Earth, if it is a deep space probe. Generally, it can be stated that the farther the spacecraft is to move from Earth, the greater the propulsion requirement, since long-distance spacecraft are necessarily larger and heavier.

Assuming that any space experiment starts from Earth (later we will cover another possibility), the types of missions that can be performed hinge largely on the power available in the launch vehicles. Initially, all launch vehicles were modified guided missiles. Later, launch vehicles especially designed for space work were developed. Now there is a large-scale U.S. effort to develop a series of space launchers of ever-increasing power. These vehicles cannot be developed overnight. They require intense re-

Ready to go: just before launch, the Echo satellite's Delta rocket vents a cloud of excess liquid oxygen. Echo, a 100-foot aluminized Mylar plastic sphere, was the first passive communications satellite. It was orbited August 12, 1960.

search and engineering effort, long periods of test, modifications based on tests, great expenditures of labor and money.

Although lunar and interplanetary exploration, particularly in manned spacecraft, hold the most fascination for the lay observer, there is still a need to boost smaller payloads into Earth orbit or near-space. The applied satellites in the fields of communication, weather forecasting, navigation, and military surveillance must still be perfected. In addition, there is still much to learn about our own Earth and close-in space.

For these closer missions, a series of relatively small launch vehicles has been developed. These vehicles have been given names by the National Aeronautics and Space Administration, which directs the U.S. space program.

Cutaway shows 92-foot, three-stage Delta launch vehicle for Echo satellite. Main rocket develops 150,000 pounds of thrust at lift-off. Echo "balloon," folded in capsule beneath nose cone, was inflated in space by water vapor.

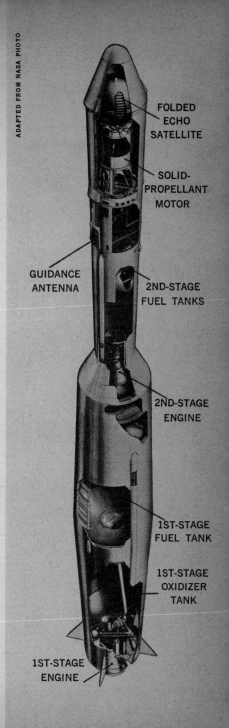

ADAPTED FROM NASA PHOTO

FOLDED
ECHO
SATELLITE

SOLID-
PROPELLANT
MOTOR

GUIDANCE
ANTENNA

2ND-STAGE
FUEL TANKS

2ND-STAGE
ENGINE

1ST-STAGE
FUEL TANK

1ST-STAGE
OXIDIZER
TANK

1ST-STAGE
ENGINE

SCOUT

There is Scout, which has four stages, all solid-propelled. Designed as a low-cost vehicle, it nonetheless costs about $750,000 per unit, an indication of the tremendous expenditures involved in space exploration. Scout can boost a 150-pound spacecraft into a near-Earth orbit (300 miles altitude). It has 115,000 pounds of thrust in its first, or bottom, stage; 55,000 pounds in the second stage; about 14,000 pounds in the third stage; and 3,000 pounds in the fourth, or top, stage. Although it is the smallest of the modern launch vehicles, Scout is seventy-two feet high — about as tall as a seven-story building. Scout is used for launching Earth satellites or sounding rockets.

DELTA

Next is Delta, which has three stages. Its first stage is a liquid-fuel Thor missile with 150,000 pounds of thrust. The second stage is a liquid-fuel rocket; the top stage is a solid-fuel rocket. Ninety-two feet high, Delta is used for medium-size Earth satellites and very small space probes. It can boost a 480-pound spacecraft into a 300-mile orbit or provide sufficient velocity to permit a 65-pound spacecraft to escape Earth's gravity.

THOR-AGENA B

Moving up the ladder, there is Thor-Agena B. This is a two-stage launch vehicle, eighty feet high. The lower stage is again the Thor missile, a booster which has demonstrated a high degree of reliability. Atop the Thor is Agena B, a liquid-fuel rocket with 15,000 pounds of thrust. Designed for boosting medium-sized Earth satellites, Thor-Agena B can send a 1,600-pound spacecraft into a 300-mile orbit.

ATLAS-AGENA B

For still larger payloads, there is Atlas-Agena B. The Agena B is again the second stage, but the first stage is the powerful

Atlas missile, which develops 360,000 pounds of thrust. Ninety-eight feet high, it can blast a two and one-half ton spacecraft into a 300-mile orbit, or it can push a smaller payload of 800 pounds beyond Earth's gravity into deep space.

CENTAUR

One step further up the ladder is Centaur. Centaur has two powerful rocket stages, the lower one being the Atlas. The second stage has two liquid-fuel rockets using a new type of fuel-oxidizer combination, liquid hydrogen and liquid oxygen. The hydrogen replaces the kerosene-type fuel used in earlier launch vehicles. This hydrogen-oxygen combination produces a higher specific impulse, hence greater power. The two rockets produce 30,000 pounds of thrust in a fairly small second stage. Despite

An experimental Centaur upper-stage vehicle rests atop modified Atlas in a gantry crane. Centaur will be first liquid hydrogen-powered spacecraft. It is designed to launch interplanetary probes, and "soft-land" instruments on moon.

NATIONAL AERONAUTICS AND SPACE ADMINISTRATION

its increased power, Centaur is only eight feet taller than Atlas-Agena B.

With Centaur, scientists will be able to perform some of the more advanced unmanned space missions. Centaur can provide escape velocity for a 1,450-pound spacecraft, and it has a very precise guidance system. It can send instrument packages to the moon, either for landing or for orbiting, and it can send a spacecraft to the vicinity of the closer planets.

SATURN

Even Centaur, with all its thrust, is not adequate for the next steps in manned space exploration. Remember, the smallest and least complex multi-man spacecraft now contemplated will weigh about ten tons. This requires a still larger launch vehicle. Such a vehicle, called Saturn, is already being developed.

Work was started on Saturn in 1958, but it will not be ready until the mid-sixties, an example of how long it takes to build one of these mighty new launch vehicles. The basic Saturn will have either two or three stages. The first stage will have 1,500,000 pounds of thrust, more than four times the thrust in the huge Atlas missile. Saturn's thrust is obtained by "clustering"; that is, grouping together eight individual engines, each producing 188,000 pounds of thrust. These engines use liquid propellants, burning liquid oxygen and a type of purified rocket propellant.

The cluster system of multiple engines is also used in the second stage. The engines are the same as those used in the second stage of Centaur. Saturn has six of them producing 90,000 pounds thrust. If the third stage is used, it will consist of two additional engines developing 30,000 pounds of thrust.

Saturn is enormous. It is 185 feet high, taller than an 18-story building! It is so large that even its first stage alone cannot be moved over rail or highway. A special barge had to be built to move it from its construction place in Alabama to its launching pad at Cape Canaveral, Florida.

With its great thrust Saturn will launch a number of important space missions. The most interesting is the multi-man space observatory. Saturn can also send a number of large-payload, unmanned experiments to the vicinity of the moon. It can also thrust a three-ton instrumented spacecraft to Mars or Venus.

Yet for manned flight around the moon, still more power will be needed. Thus an advanced model of Saturn is being planned. For this version, a huge rocket engine is now under development. In a single chamber, this engine will produce as much thrust as all eight engines of the basic Saturn — 1,500,000 pounds. The advanced Saturn will employ two such engines in the lower stage, for a total thrust output of 3,000,000 pounds. In the second stage, four of the 200,000-pound-thrust hydrogen

NATIONAL AERONAUTICS AND SPACE ADMINISTRATION

Ranger I, first in family of unmanned spacecraft designed for exploration of moon and planets, was launched by this Atlas-Agena B two-stage rocket August 23, 1961. Later Rangers are to "hard-land" instrument packages on the moon.

engines will be clustered for an additional 800,000 pounds of thrust. The third stage will have six engines with a total thrust of 90,000 pounds. The advanced Saturn is being designed to hurl fifty tons into Earth orbit or send twelve tons on a one-way trip to Mars.

The advanced Saturn launch vehicle will make possible a trip *around* the moon in a multi-man spacecraft by about 1965. However, the spacecraft will not be able to land on the moon. To do so would require much more payload in terms of rocket propellant for braking on the descent to the moon's surface and for the all-important return trip, including more braking power for re-entry into Earth's atmosphere.

You can see how demanding are the power requirements for space exploration, when even a huge launcher like the advanced Saturn is not capable of handling the man-on-the-moon assignment. And this is only an early step to real space conquest. For the manned lunar landing, and for long-distance space probes, a vehicle which dwarfs even mighty Saturn is planned.

NOVA

This super-launch vehicle bears the tentative code name of Nova. It may be either liquid- or solid-fueled. In one version, the first stage is powered by eight of the large 1,500,000-pound-thrust liquid-fuel rockets used in the advanced Saturn. Clustering eight of these engines would provide Nova with 12,000,000 pounds of thrust in the bottom stage alone. Nova would also have one or more upper stages. In fact, the entire advanced Saturn may become just an upper stage for Nova.

Nova might also employ large solid-fuel rockets, which have certain advantages over liquid-fuel rockets. However, although the 1,500,000-pound-thrust single-chamber liquid-fuel rocket is already well along in development, research in such very powerful solid-fuel rockets is not as far along. Final decision as to form of propulsion and number of stages has not been reached. Many experiments are needed to obtain the necessary data.

In any event, Nova will be a king-sized launch vehicle. In a three-stage liquid-fuel rocket form, it would stretch nearly 300 foot into the air, almost the length of a football field. With 12,000,000 pounds of thrust in the lower stage, it could launch the manned lunar-landing spacecraft and send large unmanned probes far into the solar system.

The Nuclear Launch Vehicle

It would seem that the incredible Nova would have to be the ultimate in launch vehicles, but it is not. There is a further step — using nuclear propulsion, a priority area of current space propulsion research.

In a nuclear rocket, a "working fluid" such as liquid hydrogen is passed through a nuclear reactor, which provides the source of heat instead of the combustion process which occurs in present rockets. The liquid hydrogen, superheated by the reactor, is changed into a gas and exhausted through a nozzle to produce thrust. This system provides far greater performance than the conventional rocket — it could increase the payload capabilities of Nova or Saturn by two to three times, opening up a whole new range of possible space missions.

But what of the real "space ships," huge craft capable of hurtling to the far reaches of our solar system, remaining in space for months or even years? Is it possible to build launch vehicles capable of blasting such spacecraft through the atmosphere and beyond the pull of gravity, when even a monstrous booster like the nuclear Nova cannot send a crew to Mars?

Theoretically, it is possible, but the mind recoils at the power, size, and cost of such a launcher. There is an alternative: the space station. Hitherto a dream of the science fiction writers, the space station is now a practical consideration in space planning.

Remember, all of the mighty power we have been discus-

The "nozzles" of giant Saturn Booster—82 feet long, 22 in diameter—fairly shout "thrust." Booster, which is most of Saturn Rocket's power plant, will be capable of placing ten tons in low Earth orbit.

sing is needed primarily to boost the spacecraft through the atmosphere and to overcome gravity. What if the spacecraft could start its voyage *beyond* the atmosphere, with gravity already neutralized? The possibilities are obviously enormous.

With no air resistance to combat, a relatively small amount of rocket thrust could accelerate a very heavy spacecraft to great speeds. The huge weight of launch vehicles could be eliminated or translated into useful payload — oxygen supplies, food and water, protective equipment, space for living quarters, and large amounts of fuel for controlling and braking the spacecraft. Such a vehicle could change course at will instead of coasting on momentum in a prearranged path.

All this would be possible if there were available a station in space. And it is possible to build such a station. It will be, in effect, a very large manned Earth-orbiting satellite, a miniature moon.

The Space Station

A permanent space station will require a crew of many men, perhaps twenty, plus the necessary artificial environment, protective equipment, and supplies for an indefinite stay in space. Thus, it will be extremely heavy and cannot be launched intact from Earth. However, it can be assembled in space by a technique known as "orbital rendezvous."

The design most frequently proposed for the permanent space station is a wheel- or doughnut-shaped structure with a hub, or core, in the center. The various sections of the station would be built on Earth, like a prefabricated house, then assembled in orbit. In the rendezvous technique, the core, or center section, would first be sent into orbit at an altitude of from 1,000 to 2,000 miles. This core would be a spacecraft similar to the observation satellites discussed in Chapter I, weighing about ten tons and containing three or four men. Then, one at a time, the other sections would be brought up to the core by a shuttle-spacecraft, operating between an Earth base and the space station. Assembling the space station in an Earth orbit requires extraordinarily precise guidance, since the shuttling spacecraft must enter the same orbit as the core of the space station and meet the core in space. It is something like throwing a ball into the air and then trying to hit it with another ball. If the shuttle-craft misses its target by a few hundred yards, it can be maneuvered into contact with the core by a short burst of rocket power.

To assemble the prefabricated sections, the astronauts will, of course, have to leave the core. They will need advanced types of space suits with a built-in pressurization and breathing system. Oxygen will be supplied by tanks strapped to the space suit, much like those used for underwater exploration. Small jets built into the suit will permit maneuvering.

The idea of constructing a large structure in space, while whirling about the Earth at a speed of about 17,000 miles an hour, is difficult to grasp. Remember, though, that there is practically no impression of speed. If you fly in a jet airliner six miles above the Earth, and look out the window, it seems as if you are almost standing still, in spite of the fact that you are moving at 600 miles an hour. The spacemen would have even less of a sensation of motion. After all, this very minute you are hurtling through space at twenty miles per second, but you are not aware of this motion because it is relative to a reference point, the sun, ninety-three million miles away. In addition, the spacemen would not have to contend with air resistance, which also causes a sensation of speed.

The huge sections of the space station, which might weigh a ton or more on Earth, weigh nothing in orbit, since gravity is counterbalanced by orbital velocity. Thus they can be nudged into position by short blasts from the space-suit jets.

In this manner, each of the prefabricated sections will be brought up from Earth and bolted into place until the space station is completely assembled. Once it is completed, shuttle-craft will continue to bring up supplies.

Someday the first space station will orbit Earth. Giant wheel-shaped structure may serve as low-gravity platform for future space launches.

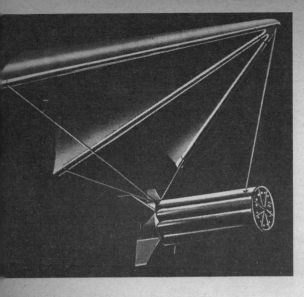

NASA PHOTO

In this artist's conception, a proposed "flexible-wing paraglider" takes spent Saturn first-stage rocket safely back to the Earth, for possible re-use. Saturn is to develop 1,500,000 pounds thrust.

The Re-Usable Launch Vehicle

For continuous resupply of the space station, another major development is required. This is the re-usable launch vehicle. The current practice of letting a multimillion-dollar launch vehicle drop into the ocean after it has boosted a spacecraft into orbit would be prohibitively expensive. It is feasible, however, to build a manned launch vehicle with wings, aerodynamic controls, and re-entry protection. A vehicle of this design could launch a spacecraft toward the permanent space station, then return to Earth to be used again.

The space station will serve as a "filling station in the sky." Since fuel is by far the major portion of any space payload, the spacecraft can take off from Earth "light," with just enough rocket fuel for maneuvering into contact with the space station. There it can take on a full load of fuel and proceed to its final destination — the moon or other planets. And, of course, the amount of fuel needed for even a very long trip is minimized, since the spacecraft starts its voyage outside the atmosphere and 2,000 miles from Earth's center of gravity.

Electrical Propulsion

There is still another step which cuts fuel requirements for spacecraft to almost nothing and makes possible even the most distant voyage within the solar system. This power system is called electrical propulsion.

The most advanced rockets can fire for only a few minutes. In that time, they consume all their fuel, but they produce tremendous thrust which permits the spacecraft to "coast" on momentum after the fuel burns up. If a spacecraft could start its journey from a permanent space station, a few pounds of thrust would suffice to get it moving.

Electrical propulsion makes possible low thrust for indefinite periods. In one design for electrical propulsion, a device such as a nuclear reactor breaks down atoms of a given substance into electrically charged particles. These charged particles can in turn be accelerated to high velocity and ejected from the vehicle by an electrostatic pumping device. Escaping at very high velocities, these particles perform the same function as the stream of hot gas in a rocket engine. They produce an *action*, and the resulting *reaction* produces thrust. Research on electrical power plants is already under way and, although it is still in its infancy, this type of propulsion appears promising.

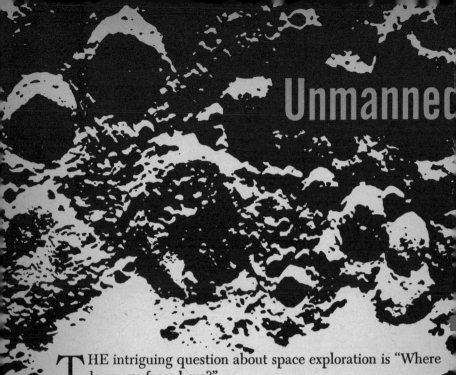

THE intriguing question about space exploration is "Where do we go from here?"

It is possible to predict, with a high probability of accuracy, the events of the next ten years in space flight, because the program for the coming decade of U.S. space exploration has already been laid out. The Soviet Union has not confided in us its plans for the next ten years, but it is most likely that the Russian program will proceed along lines similar to ours.

To start with, throughout the decade there will be a long succession of sounding rockets and unmanned Earth satellites designed to acquire specific information and to perfect some of the applied space systems discussed earlier. We will omit detailed discussion of these programs in order to devote the space available to the more exciting lunar and interplanetary programs.

CHAPTER 8

Exploration of the Moon

Throughout the decade of the sixties, the moon will be Target Number One. From the scientific standpoint, the moon is a treasure house of information, a perfect laboratory for discoveries relating to such intriguing problems as the origin of our solar system, the development of the stars, and the formation of matter.

On Earth, the surface has changed constantly over the centuries, the result of erosion caused by rivers and oceans, winds, rain, and other types of weather. In the solar system the moon, however, is still in a "mint" condition. It has existed, at best estimates, for four and one-half billion years. It is believed to have no atmosphere, no eroding waters, and no winds. Thus, it is probably unworn. Except for the peppering of its surface by meteors, the moon has remained virtually unchanged for millions of centuries.

Aside from the knowledge to be gained by intense investigation of the moon, it has a tremendous value for deep space exploration. It is a natural "space station" much larger than anything man can build in space. It offers a potential base for deep penetration of the solar system. The absence of both atmospheric drag and strong gravitational force permits a very low escape velocity. A spacecraft can leave the moon's surface with minimal thrust requirements. It is even possible that, after establishment of a lunar base, man may discover materials which will permit manufacture of rocket fuel on the moon, eliminating the need to transport fuel from Earth.

The moon is a natural target because it is our nearest neighbor in space; its average distance from Earth is about 240,000 miles. It has a diameter of 2,160 miles, approximately one-fourth that of Earth. Its gravity is about one-sixth that of Earth, and the escape velocity needed is only slightly more than 5,000 miles per hour.

The first steps in lunar exploration will be unmanned. The unmanned portion of the moon program will be carried out in three stages, each bearing a code name. These steps have been in preparation for some time and the first unmanned U.S. spacecraft is scheduled to land on the moon in 1962 or early 1963.

The Ranger Program

This first lunar probe is called Ranger. The spacecraft is difficult to describe, since it is nothing more than a collection of carefully arranged equipment. Remember, once the spacecraft leaves Earth's atmosphere, it encounters no air resistance all the way to the moon's surface. There is no need for the streamlining traditionally associated with science-fiction spacecraft.

The Ranger spacecraft consists of a six-sided "barrel" containing the scientific equipment and controls. Protruding from two sides of the barrel are long solar paddles, each ten square feet in area, covered with solar cells which trap radiant energy from the sun and convert it to power for the various items of equipment.

On the top and bottom of the spacecraft are antenna "dishes." The lower antenna is pointed at Earth so that signals can be sent from a ground station to the spacecraft. The upper antenna points at the sun, so that the paddles will catch the sun's energy. The spacecraft is equipped with "sensors," which "study" the position of Ranger relative to the Earth and sun. If the spacecraft deviates from the proper position, the sensors send signals to small steering jets, which fire briefly and bring the spacecraft back into position so that the antennas are always pointed properly.

The lunar-landing Ranger is actually two spacecraft in one package. The main spacecraft is called the "bus." Inside the bus is a second spacecraft, a thirty-inch sphere containing scientific instruments, with a small rocket attached to it. The main spacecraft is designed to make a "hard" landing on the moon. It will crash onto the lunar surface at high speed, so the experiments it will make must be conducted swiftly as it approaches the moon.

The spherical second spacecraft will separate from the main spacecraft prior to landing and make a "semihard" landing. The rockets of the second spacecraft will brake the fall as it hurtles toward the surface, and the instruments within the sphere will be protected by padding and a wall of liquid to cushion the shock. The instruments are designed to operate after landing.

The basic Ranger spacecraft, designed for hard lunar landing. Extended "wings" contain hundreds of solar cells, which intercept energy from the sun and convert it to electric power for instruments. An advanced version incorporates second small spacecraft, as a separate "back-down" rocket for a semihard landing.

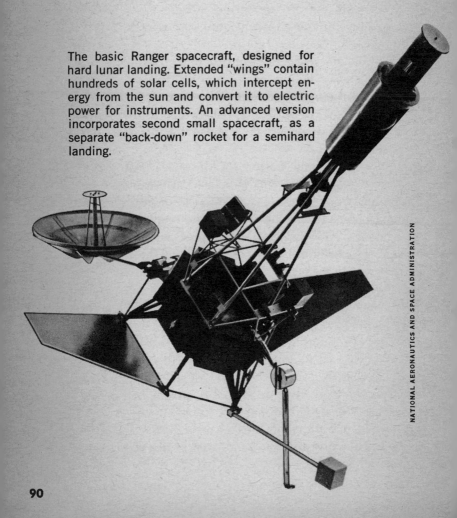

NATIONAL AERONAUTICS AND SPACE ADMINISTRATION

The entire main spacecraft is about twelve feet tall and weighs about 800 pounds. It is equipped with telemetering devices to send back information to Earth on "command." That is, a signal from Earth can start the scientific equipment working. The semihard landing sphere also has telemetering equipment.

Ranger will conduct a number of experiments. The initial Rangers, launched in 1961 and 1962, will not land on the moon. Intended primarily to test the basic design, they explore interplanetary space and the region between Earth and the moon. These first Rangers do not have the spherical auxiliary spacecraft. Instead, they have instruments to send back data on radiation, on the Earth's magnetic field, and on the hydrogen layer which encircles the Earth.

The advanced Rangers, which will impact the moon in "hard landing," contain a television camera which will take close-up pictures of the lunar surface as the spacecraft approaches the moon. They also have a gamma ray spectrometer to determine whether the moon's crust has a high concentration of radioisotopes. The auxiliary spacecraft, or spherical landing capsule, contains a seismometer, a device such as is used on Earth to record earthquake tremors. It will send back data on lunar quakes, volcanoes, or other disturbances within the crust of the moon.

The Ranger spacecraft will be launched by the Atlas-Agena B launch vehicle described in the preceding chapter. The initial velocity, as the spacecraft leaves Earth, will be just under 25,000 miles per hour. This is considered the best speed for a lunar mission; if the spacecraft started out at a higher speed, it would be going too fast when it reached the moon. At a lower speed, of course, it could not escape from Earth and hence would not reach the moon. Ranger will take sixty-five hours to reach the moon. Since the moon is moving around the Earth, the spacecraft is not aimed directly at the moon, but rather at a point in space where the moon will be sixty-five hours after the time of launch.

A Typical Ranger Flight

Here is the flight sequence for a Ranger lunar mission.

The Atlas-Agena B boosts the spacecraft to an altitude of 350 miles and a speed of close to 25,000 miles per hour. On the way through the atmosphere, the spacecraft is covered by a streamlined metal shroud to minimize the effects of air resistance. In space, the shroud falls off automatically, the launch vehicle separates, and the spacecraft starts on its path toward the moon rendezvous.

After the launch, Ranger will coast on momentum. On a signal from Earth, the solar paddles (which were folded into the barrel at launch) are lowered into position. On another signal, the sensors go into action and line up the spacecraft so that its Earth antenna and its solar antenna are properly aligned.

Meanwhile, ground stations track the flight of the Ranger by radio telescopes. At about the halfway mark, controllers on Earth compare the path of the spacecraft with the actual moon trajectory to see if Ranger is on course. If it is not, they send a signal which fires the spacecraft's steering rockets and corrects its course. At this point, the gamma ray spectrometer starts operating.

All this time the spacecraft is gradually losing speed, because it is still in Earth's gravitational field. The farther it moves from Earth, the weaker the pull of Earth gravity. Sixty hours from Earth, it will reach a point about 24,000 miles from the moon — nine tenths of the total distance from Earth to the moon. At this point, the spacecraft has slowed down to slightly more than 1,000 miles per hour. But now the moon's gravity captures the spacecraft and starts to pull the Ranger toward the surface of the moon, accelerating it once again.

Now the controllers on Earth send another series of commands. First, the Ranger must be turned around so that the braking rocket in the landing capsule is pointed at the surface of the moon. This is accomplished by firing short bursts on the control jets. Another signal sets the television camera in action.

RANGER TRAJECTORY

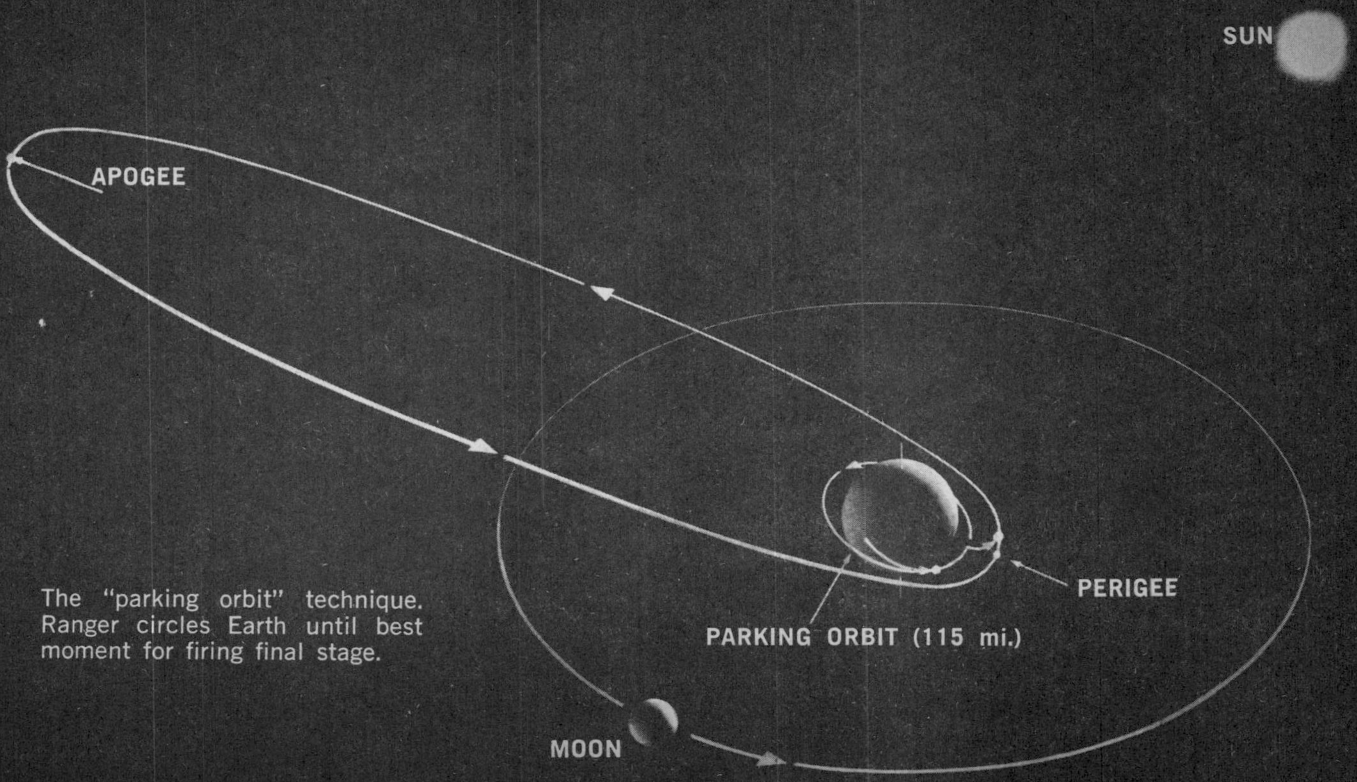
SUN
APOGEE
PERIGEE
PARKING ORBIT (115 mi.)
MOON

The "parking orbit" technique. Ranger circles Earth until best moment for firing final stage.

NATIONAL AERONAUTICS AND SPACE ADMINISTRATION

Under the influence of lunar gravity, the spacecraft hurtles moonward, its telemetry equipment sending back television images of the moon's surface as it "rushes up" to meet the spacecraft. Within the Ranger is a radio altimeter, which measures the height of the spacecraft above the moon's surface. When the spacecraft reaches the desired altitude (about 100 miles), the altimeter in the spacecraft sends a signal which sets off the rocket in the landing capsule and ejects the capsule from the main spacecraft. After the ejection, the TV camera ceases operation.

The main spacecraft, its job done, crashes onto the surface of the moon. The second spacecraft (landing sphere), its reverse rocket thrust slowing it up, makes a more gradual descent and hits the moon with a jarring but not destructive impact. Its seismometer starts to send back data, and continues to do so for about three months.

The Surveyor Program

There will be six or seven Ranger impact missions before the next step in lunar exploration is undertaken. Step Two is the more difficult "soft" landing with delicate and much more complex instruments, to be accomplished by a spacecraft called Surveyor.

Though larger and much heavier than Ranger, the Surveyor spacecraft is similar to Ranger in shape, or rather in lack of definable shape. It is simply a structure containing a battery of instruments, sensors, control jets, and other equipment. Surveyor contains many more instruments than Ranger, and its instruments are more sophisticated, or "intelligent."

Surveyor is thirteen feet tall and weighs about 2,600 pounds. To boost this weight to the moon, the Centaur launch vehicle, more powerful than the Atlas-Agena B, is needed.

The center section of the Surveyor contains a large rocket engine and its fuel tanks. This is the rocket which permits the "soft" landing. It fires continuously throughout the descent to

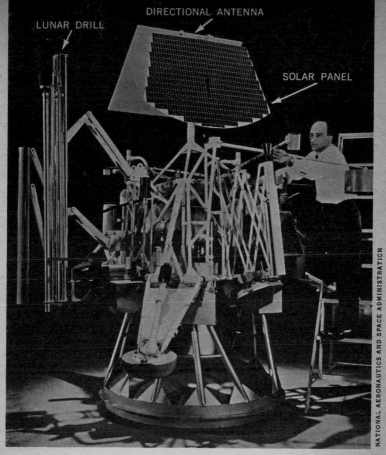

LUNAR DRILL   DIRECTIONAL ANTENNA

SOLAR PANEL

NATIONAL AERONAUTICS AND SPACE ADMINISTRATION

Model Surveyor shows instruments to take samples on moon.

the moon, its braking thrust permitting the spacecraft to "back down" to a gentle landing. Protruding from the structure are three "landing legs," each equipped with a shock-absorbing system such as those used on the wheel struts of an airliner. These legs take up the landing shock and also allow the spacecraft to remain upright after landing.

Surveyor will perform a number of experiments on the surface of the moon. It is instrumented to take radiation readings, record data about magnetism on the moon, record temperatures, and collect information on the internal structure of the moon. Special instruments, propelled by a gas jet, can be projected about fifteen feet away from the main structure so that they will not interfere with other experiments and will not record any possible contamination of the lunar surface by the braking rocket's gas. Fifteen feet is considered an adequate distance because of lack of atmosphere to spread the contamination.

For a complete look at the moon's surface in the landing area, Surveyor has a very advanced television system. There are four separate television cameras, one directly beneath the spacecraft as it stands upright and three others located adjacent to each of the landing legs. Instead of pointing at the moon's

NATIONAL AERONAUTICS AND SPACE ADMINISTRATION

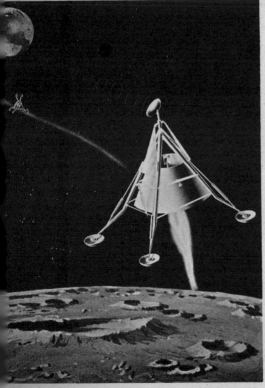

The "soft-landing" technique for unmanned lunar spacecraft is shown in this artist's conception. As spacecraft nears the moon, signals from Earth orient it so that its rocket thrust is directed downward—toward moon's surface. Rocket is fired and spacecraft "backs down" on thrust column. Descent speed is about five miles an hour. Shock absorbers on landing legs cushion impact.

surface, these cameras are aimed at movable mirrors directly above them. The mirrors can be turned in any direction by a signal from Earth, permitting 360-degree coverage of the lunar landing area. Like Ranger, Surveyor will also take pictures as it descends to the moon's surface, but better images are expected since it will be descending slowly.

The Lunar Drill

The most fascinating of Surveyor's many experiments is the "lunar drill," an instrument which will permit the very important examination of the surface and subsurface composition of the moon. This will provide a number of vital scientific clues. Is the moon composed of the same material as Earth? Does it have the elements necessary for the manufacture of rocket fuel? What is its internal temperature? Does it have a molten core like Earth? What is its internal structure?

The lunar drill is one of the most ingenious instruments ever devised. The drill itself, built something like an oil drill, is sixty inches long. Mounted on a retractable arm, it extends several feet away from the spacecraft. It makes a hole one and three-quarter inches in diameter and five feet deep. The surface material extracted from the moon's surface is forced by pressure up a chute and into a pulverizer, which grinds it into a fine powder. The material then passes through a set of four instruments, each of which makes a specific test to determine the presence or absence of certain elements. The findings of each instrument are translated into a coded signal which is telemetered back to Earth for analysis. Power for the drill, and for all the other instruments and the telemetry equipment, is provided by a combination of solar cells and batteries.

The flight sequence for a Surveyor mission is similar to that of Ranger, except for the use of the Centaur vehicle as the launcher. Nine tenths of the way to the moon, the spacecraft is "oriented," or turned around, so that the thrust blast of the rocket engine is pointed toward the surface of the moon. Again,

Artist's conception of one possible Prospector space-craft design: a roving vehicle or "moon crawler." After soft landing, instrumented, tool-equipped craft would move about on large balloon tires, perform experiments "commanded" by radio from Earth.

the radio altimeter ignites the rocket, but this time there is no capsule separation, as in Ranger. The rocket continues to fire all the way to the lunar surface. Its thrust is carefully precalculated so that it is slightly lower than the amount needed to balance lunar gravity. The rocket thrust would normally force the spacecraft upward, but lunar gravity is exerting a slightly stronger downward force. The net result is a slow backing-down action. The spacecraft will bump the surface at a descent speed of only five miles an hour, and even this slight jolt is cushioned by the shock-absorbing landing legs. Then Surveyor's fascinating instruments go to work exploring the moon without any help from man, other than the radio signals coming 240,000 miles through space from Earth.

The Moon-Orbiting Surveyor

There are certain experiments which need to be performed *above* the moon, rather than on the surface; for instance, detailed mapping of the lunar surface to discover terrain features which cannot be seen by Earth telescopes. For this and other experiments in connection with the moon's magnetic field and radiation in the space above the moon, there is an alternate version of Surveyor. This does not land on the lunar surface but instead goes into orbit around the moon.

In this version, the lunar drill and other surface instruments are replaced by a different instrumentation and the landing legs are eliminated. The flight sequence is the same until it comes time to orient the spacecraft. At this point, signals from Earth will turn the spacecraft to the proper position for a lunar orbit and the rocket will be ignited. Surveyor will be traveling too fast to go into orbit, since a lunar orbit requires a much lower speed (less than 5,000 miles per hour) than an Earth orbit. The job of the rocket, then, is to fire in reverse direction and slow the spacecraft to orbital speed. Target dates for Surveyor missions are 1963-65.

The Prospector Program

After Surveyor comes a still more advanced unmanned lunar-exploration spacecraft called Prospector.

Actually, Prospector is the name of a project given a whole series of spacecraft rather than one specific design. It is impossible to describe any one of these spacecraft, since the designs have not yet been completed. However, space scientists have mapped out the types of missions Prospector will perform.

The first type of Prospector spacecraft is designed for a very detailed photographic survey of the moon, taken at a very low altitude. Such a vehicle can answer a lot of questions that have puzzled astronomers for years. For instance, telescope observers occasionally notice slight blurs in the bottoms of moon craters. Can these blurs be carbon dioxide clouds, as has been theorized? There are also dark streaks radiating from certain craters. Can they be due to some primitive form of plant life?

The low-altitude-survey spacecraft can send back pictorial data to unlock these and a number of other lunar mysteries.

For this mission, the Prospector spacecraft will be a "hovercraft," that is, it will be able to hover over the moon like a helicopter and skip about from one location to another. It will have a number of powerful rocket engines to enable it to back down to the moon like Surveyor, but when it reaches photographic altitude (perhaps fifty or a hundred feet), the thrust will be adjusted so that it drops no lower. It will hang in space, supported by its rockets, as a helicopter hangs on its rotor blades. Its battery of television cameras will go into action, photographing the surface from every angle. Then, on a signal from Earth, control jets will move the spacecraft to another position. When the rocket fuel is nearly exhausted, the spacecraft will be permitted to land on the surface, where a separate battery of instruments will start transmitting surface data.

Another Prospector version is the "roving vehicle," which crawls about the surface of the moon recording and transmitting data as it goes. The vehicle will have large balloon tires or tank treads for moving over the lunar terrain and it will have a separate engine for "moon crawling." Its instruments will be similar to those in Surveyor, and the roving vehicle can be stopped and started by a signal from Earth, permitting samplings from many different parts of the lunar surface.

Returnable Unmanned Lunar Spacecraft

The third type of Prospector will contain "returnable capsules," that is, small spacecraft which can return to Earth from the moon, carrying samples of surface material for detailed analysis in Earth laboratories. In this version, the main spacecraft will back down to the moon on rocket thrust as in the other missions. A lunar drill will extract a surface sample and convey it to a capsule. The capsule is equipped with a large rocket engine, powerful enough to escape from the moon's gravity and enter a trajectory back to Earth.

Once the capsule is loaded with moon material, a sensor "tells" the ground station back on Earth. Earth controllers then send a signal which ignites the rocket and sends the capsule into its homeward path. The capsule will be a miniature spacecraft with its own control jets, power supply, and transmitting equipment. It will send out a continuous signal during its long voyage home. Thus, the ground controllers can track it and correct its course if necessary. After it plunges through the upper atmosphere, protected by a heat shield, it will be lowered to Earth by parachute. The main Prospector spacecraft will carry at least two — possibly three or four — of these returnable capsules.

The final mission planned for Prospector is that of cargo carrier, to be used in conjunction with manned landings. After man has developed the capability of staying on the moon for extended periods, Prospector "space trucks" can bring up additional supplies which could not be carried in the manned spacecraft.

Whatever their final designs, the various types of Prospectors will be large spacecraft, weighing up to ten tons when they start their trips to the moon and three or four Earth tons on the surface of the moon, after they have consumed most of their rocket fuel. Neither Atlas-Agena B nor Centaur can launch a payload of that size, so that Prospector spacecraft will have to wait for final development of the Saturn launch vehicle or perhaps, in some of the more complex missions, the advanced Saturn. No specific timetable has been set for Prospector, but the best estimate is 1967-69. During that period, space scientists will be paving the way for the spectacular, exciting manned lunar landing, expected to come at the end of this decade.

Manned Exploration

of the  Moon

THIS nation has undertaken to attempt to put man on the moon by the end of this decade, or by December 31, 1969. It is possible that this target date may be bettered by a year or more, but the program cannot be speeded up appreciably because of the massive technological problems involved in a lunar landing and return to Earth.

Before the lunar landing can be attempted, scientists must learn more about the space between Earth and its moon. In particular, they must know more about the various types of radiation and how dangerous they may be, and the frequency of micrometeorites and the chances of their puncturing the spacecraft hull. Scientists must also learn more about the moon itself and study in detail the hazards to human life on the moon. They must even select a lunar landing field.

In addition, there is still much to be learned about the physiology of man during space flight. And from the technological standpoint — the actual construction of the spacecraft

CHAPTER 9

and its launching vehicle — a simple listing of the problems to be solved would take up several pages of this book.

The lunar-landing mission will be preceded by a long succession of manned space flights. Under Project Mercury, manned Earth-orbital flights will continue for two to three years. In the Mercury capsule, astronauts will venture into orbits farther and farther from Earth and remain in space up to Mercury's maximum capability of twenty-eight hours. These flights will provide much, but not all, of the required physiological data.

Dyna-Soar

A separate manned space-flight program, called Dyna-Soar, will get under way about 1964. Dyna-Soar is what is known as a "boost-glide" spacecraft. A small, one-man craft, it is boosted into space by a launch vehicle to a speed just short of orbital velocity. This speed is sufficient to allow the Dyna-Soar to coast around the Earth several times, then spiral down to the surface. The Dyna-Soar spacecraft has wings and control jets and resembles a small airplane. Unlike the Mercury capsule, which is lowered to Earth by parachute, the Dyna-Soar can be flown down to a controlled landing. This type of spacecraft will contribute information in the vital area of re-entry into the Earth's atmosphere.

Project Apollo

The manned lunar-landing program is known as Project Apollo. It consists of three distinct steps:

First, there will be a series of Earth-orbital flights in the three-man Apollo spacecraft with flight durations up to fourteen days. These flights will serve a number of purposes. They will permit the training of space crews; the many complex systems within the spacecraft will be thoroughly tested; and information on the behavior of the human body over extended periods in space will be obtained. During the Earth-orbital flights, techniques of controlling the spacecraft will be fully developed and the spacecraft will be used as a laboratory for astronomical observations above Earth's layer of atmosphere, which distorts observations made from the surface.

In the second phase of the Apollo program, the spacecraft will be flown to greater and greater distances from Earth, culminating in a "circumlunar" flight, or a trip around the moon. On this flight, the crew will be able to study the moon up close. They will also perform many of the vital guidance and control tasks that will be needed on the moon-landing mission, including the high-speed re-entry into Earth's atmosphere and the subsequent landing.

Phase Three will be the greatest adventure of all time, the manned lunar landing.

Major Considerations for Manned Lunar Landing

Before discussing the Apollo spacecraft, let us consider some of the major problems of the manned lunar-landing mission.

First, there is the launch-vehicle requirement. The spacecraft will weigh, on departure from Earth, between sixty and seventy-five tons. The launch vehicle will have to hurl that great weight into space, and also accelerate the spacecraft to escape velocity, about 25,000 miles per hour. This requires use of the Nova super-booster, either liquid- or solid-fueled.

Navigation, which is a problem even in Earth orbit, will be a vital consideration in the lunar-landing mission. The spacecraft will not just "hit the moon"; it must land in a precise spot selected in advance. An unmanned spacecraft like Surveyor will pave the way. With its lunar drill it will find a site hard enough to sustain a manned landing, and with its multiple television cameras it will make sure the site is free of obstacles which might damage the manned spacecraft on landing. Surveyor will also leave a radio beacon on the lunar landing field, so that the Apollo navigator can "home" on its radio signals.

Starting with an initial velocity of 25,000 miles per hour, the Apollo spacecraft must follow a very accurate course to the

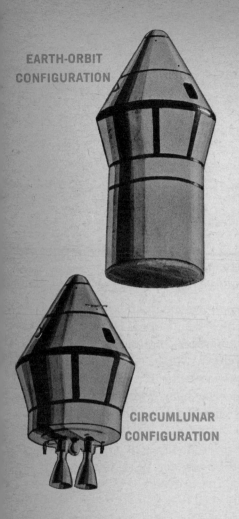

At top, a possible design for a manned Earth-orbiting Apollo spacecraft, with conical "command" section and cylindrical observatory and living quarters. Moon-circling version, below, omits observatory and substitutes a rocket system for course-correction power.

lunar landing field. By taking star fixes, the navigator will be able to determine how close he is to the preplanned path. Midway to the moon a correction can be made by firing control rockets.

However, the amount of correction which can be made is limited, because the supply of rocket fuel is limited. The spacecraft must carry fuel for correction, fuel for slowing the craft as it approaches the moon, fuel for a controlled landing, fuel for a lunar take-off, and fuel for braking again as it returns to Earth. With this fuel limitation, the navigator cannot make very large course corrections, nor can he make frequent corrections. Thus, the manned lunar-landing mission will call for extremely exact navigation techniques that minimize error.

Re-entry into the Atmosphere

Re-entry into Earth's atmosphere is critical. As the spacecraft returns from the moon, Earth's gravity will cause it to accelerate until it reaches the same speed at which it escaped from Earth, 25,000 miles per hour. The re-entry heat encountered at this speed is much more severe than that encountered on a satellite landing. To combat it effectively, the spacecraft must return to Earth in a narrow "corridor." This corridor might be compared with the landing path of an airplane as it approaches a runway. If the plane comes in too low, it will land short of the runway; too high and it will overshoot the runway. In the case of the lunar spacecraft, the "landing path" is a corridor approximately one hundred miles wide approaching Earth's atmosphere at an angle of about forty-five degrees. If the spacecraft re-enters on the low side of this corridor, it will strike the atmosphere at too severe an angle, causing excessive heating as a result of friction and probable disintegration. If it comes in too high, on the upper side of the corridor, it will only skim the atmosphere and will not slow down sufficiently for a re-entry. It would, instead, "bounce" off the top of the atmosphere and hurtle back into space on a wide elliptical path. So, again, there is the requirement for highly accurate navigation and control before a lunar landing is made.

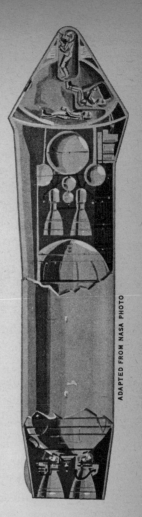

ADAPTED FROM NASA PHOTO

LUNAR-LANDING CONFIGURATION

A complete lunar-landing Apollo might look like this. Men live in the cone-shaped section. Escape rockets for return to Earth are in next section below. Bottom section has large rocket motor for soft "backdown" landing on moon. If enough thrust is available, observatory may be added.

The Solar Flare

Radiation is a minor problem on Earth-orbital missions, because the spacecraft can stay below the radiation belts surrounding the Earth. On the moon voyage, the spacecraft must pass through these belts. Protection can be provided for this type of radiation, but there is an even greater problem in the "solar flare."

The solar flare is a storm on the surface of the sun, which sends out radiation for hundreds of millions of miles. These storms occur frequently, but fortunately nearly all of them are minor flares, and protection for the astronauts can be built into the spacecraft.

Occasionally, however, there is a *giant* solar flare, which sends out radiation so intense that the weight of shielding material would be prohibitive in the Apollo spacecraft. The only apparent solution to this problem is to develop a technique for predicting the build-up of a giant flare, then postpone the lunar flight. In the past ten years, only seven giant solar flares have been observed, but an unexpected super "sun storm" could be disastrous to a lunar mission.

Weightlessness

The phenomenon of weightlessness which occurs during space flight is still an enigma to space scientists. In early manned flights, it has proved to be no problem, but rather a pleasant sensation. However, these flights were of short duration. There is still the question of whether prolonged weightlessness, for more than two days en route to the moon and two more days on the way back, might not bring on nausea, disorientation, or other illness. Such illness could be so severe that the astronauts would not be able to perform the intricate navigation and control functions required of them.

The answer to this question will be found either in the continuing series of Mercury flights or the first phase of Project

Apollo. If it appears that weightlessness is a problem, the solution lies in providing the spacecraft with an artificial "gravity," so that the astronauts will have at least a portion of their normal Earth weight. This can be accomplished by a mechanical device which spins the spacecraft around its axis slowly, at about one revolution per minute.

General Features of the Apollo Spacecraft

The final design of the Apollo spacecraft has not yet been determined. While unmanned spacecraft and manned Mercury capsules are performing the preliminary research, the Apollo design will be changed and refined many times. When the best possible configuration is agreed upon, the "go-ahead" will be given for the start of construction.

It is, however, possible to describe the Apollo spacecraft in general terms. Because of its three-phase assignment, Apollo is designed on the "building-block" concept, meaning that there are four separate major sections which can be used in any combination. The central building block is called the "command center." This is the main capsule which houses the crew during launch and landing.

In one design under study, this command center is bell-shaped, resembling a larger version of the Mercury capsule. It will have retractable stub wings, or flaps, for control within Earth's atmosphere after the return from the moon or from orbit, because, unlike Mercury, the Apollo spacecraft will be able to land at a preselected site. It will have a heat shield of an advanced type, for protection against very high re-entry temperatures. For the slow descent to the surface after the re-entry phase, the capsule will be lowered either by two large parachutes (it is too heavy for a single chute) or by a power-driven rotor, such as the rotary wing of a helicopter.

The command center will be about the size of a small room. It will have flight stations for each of the three astronauts, plus

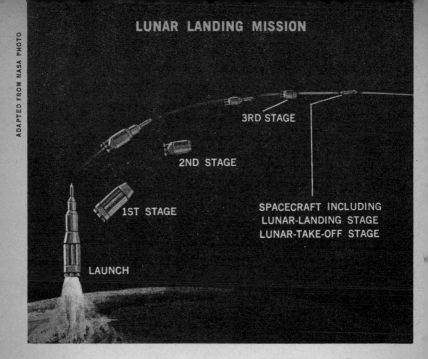

ADAPTED FROM NASA PHOTO

LUNAR LANDING MISSION

3RD STAGE

2ND STAGE

1ST STAGE

SPACECRAFT INCLUDING
LUNAR-LANDING STAGE
LUNAR-TAKE-OFF STAGE

LAUNCH

Diagram of a launching sequence for an Apollo moon-landing mission, using a Nova launch vehicle. Nova's first two stages would fall back to Earth after burnout. Third stage would escape Earth with Apollo capsule, but would not be guided to moon along with Apollo.

limited room in which to move about. It will weigh between 15,000 and 20,000 pounds.

A remarkable aspect of the Apollo spacecraft is the fact that the crew will *not* wear space suits. Space suits such as those used in Project Mercury become uncomfortable after a time. For one thing, the pressure provided in the Mercury suit is only slightly more than one-third normal Earth-surface pressure, adequate for one-day missions in space but not for two-week missions such as Apollo will perform. The Apollo command center will be pressurized at about two-thirds normal sea-level pressure, permitting the crew to operate in "shirtsleeve environment" for as long as fourteen days.

The systems within the capsules will generally be similar to those in the Mercury capsule, but of much more advanced design. In addition to the pressurization and the breathing oxygen system, the capsule will have air conditioning, equipment to remove exhaled carbon dioxide, water vapor, and other wastes, plus food and water supplies. The protective equipment will necessarily be much more complex than that of Mercury, because (1) it must provide an artificial environment for three men instead of one, and (2) it must operate flawlessly for fourteen days. The capsule will be completely sealed. Its oxygen and water must be used over and over in a "recycling" process.

The Moon Suit

Although space suits will not be used in flight, they will be on board for emergency use and for the lunar landing. Again, the suit will be far more complex than the Mercury suit. It will have to operate independently of the systems in the command center, since the astronauts will have to leave the capsule to explore the moon. The suit will have external tanks of oxygen for breathing and pressure, and its own compression and pumping system to force the oxygen into the suit. It will also have built-in communications equipment, so that the astronauts can talk to each other or to the Earth control station.

The command center will have all the controls for guiding and maneuvering the spacecraft, and, of course, a very accurate navigation system augmented by an electronic computer to help the navigator make the necessary calculations.

Protection Against Radiation

Radiation protection will be provided in a number of ways. First, all of the spacecraft's complicated equipment will be compactly grouped around the crew stations, so that the metal in these systems will afford a degree of protection. Secondly, the spacecraft must carry large supplies of water for drinking, cooling, and other purposes. These water tanks can also be arranged around the crew stations, since water can reflect some radiation. The crew will also wear water-filled jackets, like life vests. Finally, there will be one or more layers of metal shielding all around the capsule, sufficient to provide protection against all radiation except giant solar flares.

The second of the four building blocks is the basic propulsion unit, a cluster of two or more fairly large rocket engines with the necessary fuel and oxidizer tanks, valves, and pumping equipment. For Apollo Phase One, the Earth-orbiting training missions, this unit provides the braking force for re-entry into the atmosphere and it is also used for maneuvering in orbit. For Phase Two, the trip around the moon, this same unit will be used to make course corrections. It can also provide the braking thrust to allow the spacecraft to enter moon orbit, and the extra thrust required for leaving the lunar orbit to return to Earth.

In the case of the lunar-landing mission, this rocket build-

NOVA

The drawing, left, depicts Nova launch vehicle, planned for expeditions to moon, Mars, or other planets. Capable of putting 70-ton load into escape orbit (90 tons into Earth orbit), the Nova system could put three men on the moon and return them to Earth. At the same time, it could leave 20 tons of supplies and equipment on the moon to support a later manned station. The first or booster stage of Nova may actually be a cluster of eight F-1 kerosene rockets. Developed originally for Saturn booster, each F-1 produces 1,500,000 pounds of thrust. The second stage would use either two F-1 engines, or eight hydrogen-fueled types of 200,000 pounds thrust each. Two hydrogen engines would make up the third stage. Using a nuclear-powered final stage, a Nova-launched probe could circle Mars and return to Earth. At right, the artist has shown Nova third-stage landing on the moon, "backing down" on its rocket thrust. This stage would carry men and their observatory.

NOVA LAUNCH VEHICLE

NOVA THIRD STAGE

ing block is the most important component of the whole space-craft. It will provide the thrust to blast the spacecraft away from the moon. Obviously, it must be the most reliable engine that can possibly be built, complete with a number of emergency systems in case of failure of any part. Should it malfunction, the crew would be stranded on the moon.

The third building block is another propulsion stage, a large and powerful rocket cluster to be used only on the lunar-landing mission. This is the power plant which will slow down the spacecraft as it approaches the moon and lower it gently to the lunar surface. This section alone, with at least four engines and tankage, will be about sixty feet long. Again, performance must be completely reliable, since failure would result in a lunar crash.

The fourth building block is a complete space observatory, containing optical and radio telescopes and instruments for making a variety of human-directed measurements in space. This section, large enough to contain the equipment and at least one crew member, will be an extension of the basic section, the command center. For the long, tedious moon mission, this section provides extra "stretching room" and sleeping area.

Thus, depending on the mission, either two, three, or four of these building blocks can be joined together. The command center and the propulsion unit will be used on all missions. The observatory will be added for special scientific Earth-orbital missions and for the lunar mission, and the large auxiliary propulsion unit will be attached for the lunar landing.

Obviously, the total weight of the complete spacecraft will vary, depending on which sections are joined, so that the launch-vehicle requirements differ. For the Earth-orbiting mission, the launch vehicle will be the basic Saturn. For the circumlunar flight, the advanced Saturn will be employed. And for the lunar landing, the huge three-stage Nova will be the launch vehicle.

Sometime in the next ten years, three men will leave Earth on the most dramatic flight in history, the lunar landing. Some of the details may be changed as a result of continuing research, but here, in general, is what it will be like.

As it rests on its launch pad, the tremendous space vehicle — mighty Nova and its payload, the lunar spacecraft — will stretch higher into the sky than a thirty-story skyscraper. On the very top, looking tiny by comparison, is the command center containing the three astronauts with the smaller "back room," the observatory, attached. Immediately below it is the basic propulsion unit. Next, proceeding downward, is the long, cylindrical multi-rocket power section for the lunar backdown, and below it the third, second, and first stages of Nova.

The multiple engines of Nova's lower stage will ignite with an incredible roar. Slowly, the huge vehicle will lift spaceward, picking up speed rapidly. Acceleration forces will push the astronauts deep into their foam-rubber couches; they will weigh, for a brief period, several times their normal poundage.

Now the lower stage has exhausted its fuel. It automatically disconnects and falls toward the Earth. For a short time, the remaining vehicle coasts upward on momentum, then the second-stage rockets ignite, pushing the vehicle still faster. More than one hundred miles up, the second stage burns out, disconnects, tumbles Earthward. Another brief coasting period and the third stage goes into action, thrusting the vehicle ever faster — 20,000, 21,000, 22,000 miles per hour!

The guidance system, which has functioned since launch, has directed the spacecraft into a very precise path. Now the third stage of the launch vehicle, its work done, separates; because its velocity is too great, it will not return to Earth but will follow the spacecraft into space. The spacecraft is on its own, coasting on momentum at 25,000 miles per hour. The astronauts are weightless; the momentous voyage has begun.

The spacemen take their stations and immediately start work on the complicated navigation problem and their scientific observations. The spacecraft continues to coast without power, gradually losing speed but still moving at a very high velocity toward its rendezvous with the moon.

For more than a day the spacecraft coasts toward the moon. The crewmen, in constant touch with Earth, describe every detail of the great flight. The navigator is constantly measuring the altitudes of the various stars, feeding the information into his computer, carefully plotting the course. On Earth, tracking stations are following the spacecraft.

During the long voyage, the astronauts take turns sleeping, strapped to their couches, so they will not float around the spacecraft, because they will be weightless all the way to the moon. Food and water are also weightless, so they will eat and drink from "squeeze containers."

It is now time for the mid-course correction. The control rockets are ignited, the correction made, and the rockets shut off.

Almost two days from Earth, it is time for the final correction. The spacecraft radio picks up the beam from the beacon at the moon landing site, deposited there a few days earlier by an unmanned spacecraft. Another blast on the control jets and the spacecraft is on "terminal approach."

Now the spacecraft must be oriented. By precise manipulation of the controls, it is turned around so that the lunar landing rockets are pointed downward. The spacecraft has slowed considerably during its two-day trip; but it is still moving at more than 2,000 miles per hour, and lunar gravity is now starting to take over, pulling Apollo moonward.

The rockets of the lunar landing stage blast out their powerful thrust. The spacecraft slows gradually, backing down to its landing site. The craggy, "pock-marked" surface of the moon comes closer, closer. The astronauts are manipulating the control jets to insure a stable descent. The main descent rockets are still blasting, overcoming the lunar gravity. The shock-absorbing landing legs are extended. With a slight jolt, the spacecraft touches down.

Man on the Moon

With awe and wonder difficult to imagine, the astronauts don moon suits and descend to the grim, forbidding, airless terrain of Earth's natural satellite. The astronauts, either pilots trained as scientists or scientists trained as spacemen, will proceed with a series of observations.

They will venture as far as they dare from the spacecraft, exploring the ancient terrain. They will weigh only one-sixth their normal weight, because of the lower lunar gravity, so even in the bulky moon suit they will be able to cover several yards in a single step. They will map the terrain features in the vicinity of their landing site and probe beneath the lunar surface. They will analyze samples of surface minerals. They will set up telescopes and study the sun and

REPUBLIC AVIATION

An experimental "moon suit," designed to protect its wearer against heat, cold, and radiation. It carries self-contained atmosphere and communications system. Tripod legs can be lowered so that wearer can rest.

the stars, unhindered by the distorting atmosphere of Earth. And, of course, with still- and motion-picture cameras, they will photograph every detail of the lunar surface. All of their findings will be relayed continuously to Earth.

The length of the astronauts' stay on the moon on this first mission has not been finally determined. Theoretically, the spacecraft and moon suits will provide a livable environment for almost ten days, but the possibility of a failure in some part of the system increases with the duration of the visit, so it appears advisable to cut the visit short. On the other hand, the lunar landing site will not always be visible to Earth radio and optical telescopes, since the moon is moving around the Earth and the Earth is itself rotating. It is important that the launch center or other Earth tracking stations watch the lunar take-off, so that Earth assistance can be provided for navigation on the return voyage. Several days might elapse before the moon is in the proper position for such tracking, so, barring emergency, the first lunar visit will probably be five days to a week.

The Homeward Voyage

Then comes the crucial return.

On the launching from Earth, there were hundreds of people on the launch pad and in the control center, checking every item to insure absolute perfection. Now there are but three. They must examine every component to insure perfect working order and plot the course for moon escape.

As it sits on the surface of the moon, the spacecraft consists of the four building blocks. On top is the command capsule, below it the observatory, next the basic propulsion unit, finally the lunar landing stage. This latter stage has done its work; is no longer needed. It is uncoupled, to remain forever on the moon, a monument to the first U.S. manned lunar landing.

Everything checked and double-checked, the escape rockets are ignited. The spacecraft — now considerably lighter, with no atmosphere to combat, and with only one sixth of Earth gravity to overcome — hurtles into space toward Earth.

Again there is the two-day journey with mid-course corrections, as the spacecraft is directed into the narrow corridor for the Earth landing. This time, however, instead of slowing gradually, it picks up speed all the way home, from slightly more than 5,000 miles per hour as it leaves the moon to 25,000 miles per hour as it reaches Earth.

A few hundred miles from Earth, the spacecraft is again oriented so that the rockets are pointed toward Earth. They are ignited, braking the spacecraft with a sudden jolt. The astronauts are again pushed down into their couches by the force of deceleration, similar to that experienced during acceleration on the Earth launch.

The propulsion unit has exhausted its fuel; it falls off, leaving only the man-carrying capsule, which plummets into the atmosphere, slowed considerably by the braking rockets but still moving at tremendous speed. The re-entry heat mounts to high intensity, but the heat shield absorbs it. Air resistance slows the capsule, until, at about 10,000 feet, it is traveling only a few hundred miles per hour. Parachutes are released, there is a slight jolt, then the capsule drops gently to the surface.

Does it sound too fantastic for belief? A few years ago, this flight would have been labeled "sheer nonsense." Today, the full-time efforts of thousands of people are being directed toward early fulfillment of this great dream. It will happen — and it will happen before you are ten years older!

Exploration of the Solar System

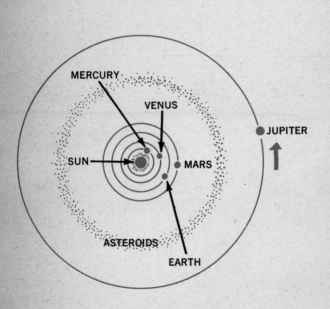

MERCURY

VENUS

JUPITER

SUN

MARS

SATURN

ASTEROIDS

EARTH

CHAPTER 10

SUCH is the inquisitive nature of the human mind, that even before the manned lunar landing becomes a reality, people will be looking beyond it to see what is next on the space agenda.

The follow-on goals are easily defined; the methods of accomplishing them are considerably less clear.

Under consideration as the next step after the initial lunar landings is construction of a permanent space station in Earth orbit. Such a station would greatly simplify the first lunar landing, by eliminating the requirement for tremendous launch vehicles like Nova and permitting a larger payload to be sent

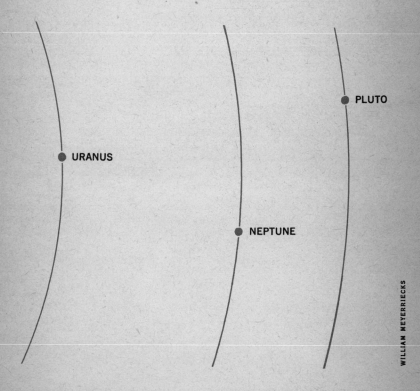

PLUTO

URANUS

NEPTUNE

WILLIAM MEYERRIECKS

Man knows only his home planet, Earth. Will he ever reach the others?

to the moon. However, starting from the point of current knowledge and technical developments, it is less difficult to launch the initial manned lunar spacecraft from Earth than it is to develop the techniques of orbital rendezvous necessary for construction of the space station. It will also take time to build the type of re-usable space truck needed to ferry the various parts into position.

During the years of preparation for the manned lunar landing, research in these areas will progress. It is possible that the large, permanent space station can be built shortly after the start of the next decade.

The Lunar Base

There is, of course, a permanent space station already available — the moon. Although space scientists have not yet determined whether the utility of a base on the moon justifies the great effort required to build it, the lunar base might prove desirable for a number of reasons. First, it may have potential as a platform for deep space penetrations by manned spacecraft. Second, a permanent moon station may have military potential in defense of our nation. Third, a thorough scientific examination of the moon can be accomplished in a relatively short time from a lunar base. To accomplish the same task by individual expeditions would take many, many years and trips.

The lunar base, then, may become the next step after the Earth-orbiting space station. With current and foreseeable technology, it should be feasible to build such a base. There are, however, many problems, chiefly the task of hauling to the moon all materials and supplies needed to create and sustain an artificial Earth environment for a great many people. Obviously, before a program of this magnitude can be started, we need a great deal more information about the moon and its environs. Such information will be obtained through the long series of manned and unmanned missions.

The Mariner spacecraft, designed for a "close" (16,000 miles) fly-by of the planet Venus. Its instruments will send back data on the magnetism, radiation, and atmospheric composition of Venus. Sun and Earth sensors combined with a cold gas jet system will keep Mariner oriented so that its solar cell paddles are always turned toward the sun and its directional antenna toward Earth. A liquid-fueled rocket motor, fired on command from Earth, will enable course corrections to be made for a close fly-by.

123

After the lunar base, the next goals are manned and unmanned investigations of our sun and of space outside the ecliptic, the plane in which Earth revolves in its orbit around the sun. The most distant space goals currently foreseeable are explorations of the other planets within the solar system, in the order of their distance from Earth: first, Venus and Mars; next, Mercury; after that Jupiter, Saturn, Uranus, Neptune, and Pluto. Also of great scientific interest are the asteroids, chunks of space matter largely concentrated between the orbit of Mars and Jupiter. Most of these asteroids are a few miles in diameter, but some are a hundred miles in diameter. The largest, known as Ceres, has a diameter of 500 miles. Since they are believed to be the remains of one or more exploded planets, they may provide important information on the origin of the solar system.

The problems of manned visits to these planets should be apparent from the foregoing discussions. They stem largely from the incredible distances involved. Thus, sending manned spacecraft to the planets will require a whole new order of technology. If we applied the lunar-mission technique (launching the spacecraft to escape velocity and permitting it to coast) to a Pluto trip, the minimum launching velocity would be 38,000 miles per hour and it would take the spacecraft forty-six years to reach the distant planet. Therefore, for practical exploration of the distant planets, the basic requirement is a propulsion system (such as electrical propulsion) capable of sustained operation over a long period and also capable of accelerating the spacecraft to such staggering speeds as a million miles or more per hour.

As for the spacecraft itself, we need not dwell on the incredible requirements. From our discussions of the relatively simple manned lunar spacecraft, you can imagine the complexity of the systems needed to sustain a crew of spacemen for voyages requiring several months, and to protect them from meteorite hits, giant solar flares and other radiation, and possible new hazards of space flight not yet discovered.

Even after the problems of interplanetary-spacecraft design and propulsion have been solved, there remain other problems. With the possible exception of Mars, the planets themselves are environments hostile to manned exploration. Mercury, nearest the sun, has surface temperatures as high as 750 degrees Fahrenheit on its "hot" side, while the other side, in perpetual darkness, has temperatures several hundred degrees below zero. Venus, next closest to the sun, has temperatures estimated at about 500 degrees and the evidence now available indicates that its atmosphere is poisonous to human beings. Massive Jupiter, more than 1,300 times the size of Earth, has an escape velocity of more than five times that of Earth, making a landing extremely hazardous and a take-off all but impossible. In addition, its tremendous gravity would crush a human being without some form of protection not yet foreseeable. The other planets offer similar natural problems, in addition to the problems of reaching them.

It is obvious, then, that even the space within our solar system will not submit readily to conquest. There are few who doubt, however, that man will eventually penetrate to the limits of our solar system. The first requirement is a greater knowledge of the planets, the space between the orbits of the planets, the sun, and the cosmic matter that comes from beyond our solar system.

The lunar-exploration program will provide considerable information in these areas. But long before the lunar landing, unmanned exploration of the planets will get under way.

The Mariner Spacecraft

The first step is a series of unmanned planetary spacecraft identified by the code name Mariner. Mariner is similar in design to the lunar Ranger, although it is larger and heavier (it will weigh slightly more than half a ton).

Mariner's initial target, in 1962, will be the planet Venus, Earth's nearest neighbor except for the moon. Because Venus is veiled by a dense cloud cover, its surface has never been seen. The surface temperature, the composition of the cloud cover, and the planet's rate of rotation about its axis — about which we can only guess — are of great scientific interest.

Boosted into space by the Centaur launch vehicle, Mariner will attain sufficient speed to escape from Earth and coast to the vicinity of Venus. It will not impact on the planet, but will make a "fly-by," passing within 27,000 miles.

One of the major instruments in the Mariner spacecraft will be a spectroscope, to examine the mysterious cloudy atmosphere of Venus and transmit data on what elements are contained in this atmosphere and in what ratio. The spectroscope will also search the Venusian atmosphere for the presence of oxygen and water vapor. Mariner will also contain a magnetometer to determine the strength of Venus' magnetic field, instruments to sample the radiation surrounding the planet and a radiometer for surface temperature readings.

After Venus, Mariner's next target is Mars. The primary question is whether life exists on the "red planet." The spacecraft will carry instrumentation similar to that for the Venus mission, with additional instruments designed to find out whether the Mars surface contains organic molecules that would indicate the presence of life. Since the Martian atmosphere is clear, like Earth's, the Mariner spacecraft will also carry television cameras to "look at" the surface of the planet. These data, when telemetered back to Earth, will provide photographic details not obtainable by Earth telescopes.

The Voyager Spacecraft

After a series of Venus and Mars missions with the Mariner spacecraft, to take place during 1962-66, a new type of spacecraft called Voyager will take over. Voyager, considerably larger and much more advanced than Mariner, will be launched

Voyager, unmanned interplanetary probe, ejects and soft-lands instruments on Mars or Venus.

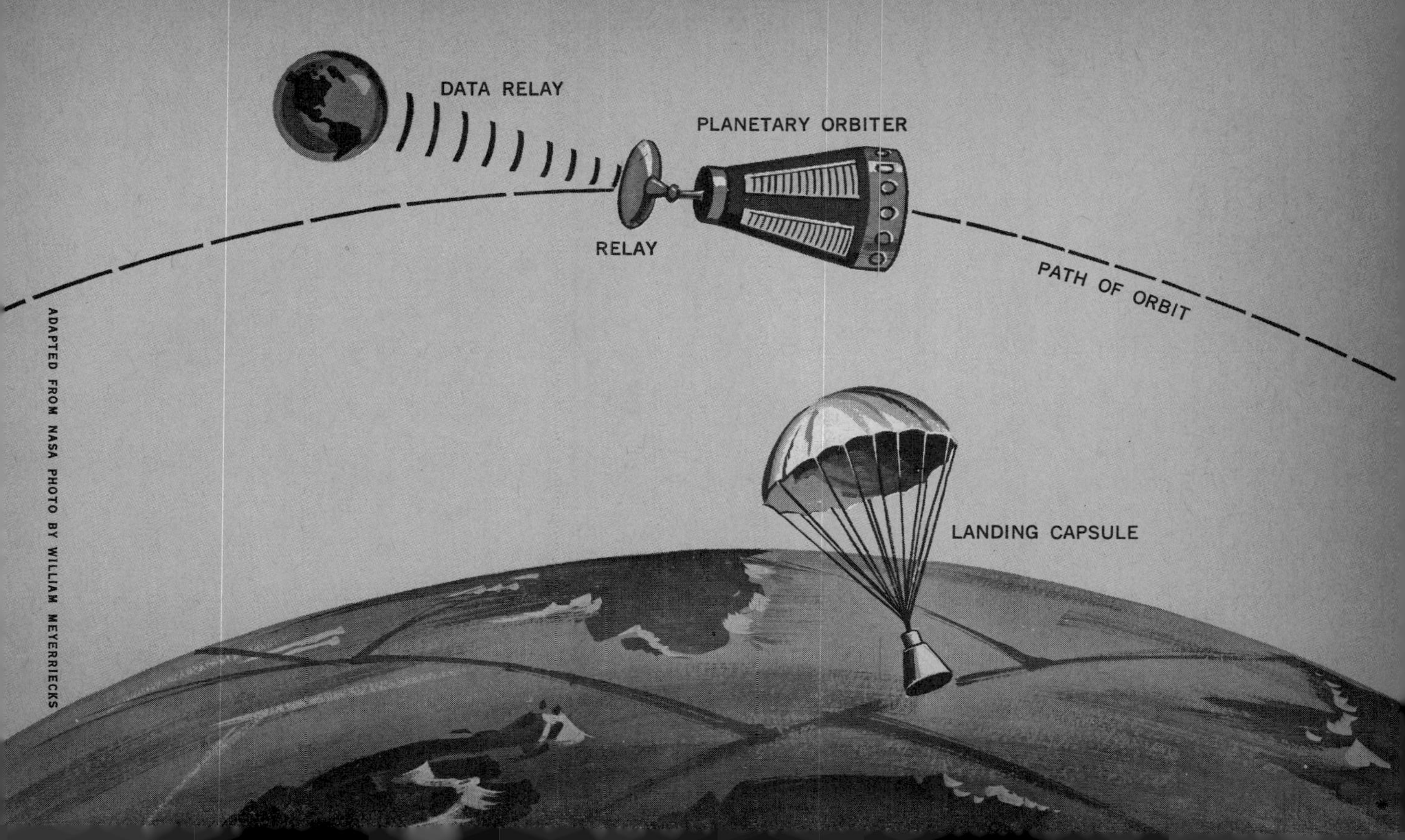

DATA RELAY

PLANETARY ORBITER

RELAY

PATH OF ORBIT

LANDING CAPSULE

ADAPTED FROM NASA PHOTO BY WILLIAM MEYERRIECKS

by the big Saturn booster. Its targets, in the years 1964-67, will also be Venus and Mars, but Voyager will be capable of acquiring more detailed information by orbiting the planets for long periods of time and continuously relaying information to Earth. Voyager will also carry a secondary spacecraft, a capsule designed to make soft landings on the planet. It will telemeter information about the lower atmospheres of the planets as it descends to a landing, and about surface conditions after landing.

Work is already proceeding on the Voyager concept, but space planners have not yet decided on the step to follow. It appears likely, however, that Venus and Mars exploration will follow the lunar pattern. If so, the follow-on program would be a large planetary spacecraft like the lunar Prospector, capable of hovering over or moving about the surfaces of Venus and Mars to add new volumes of data about our neighbor planets. Since both Venus and Mars have atmosphere, spacecraft of this type would need aerodynamic lift features and entry-heating protection. In design they would more closely resemble manned spacecraft like Apollo than unmanned vehicles such as Surveyor and Mariner.

Deep Space Probes

In the latter part of the decade of the sixties, we can expect the start of a similar series of missions to Mercury and Jupiter, the next nearest planets to Earth. Here again the step-by-step procedure, employing spacecraft of increasing sophistication, will be followed.

And, after Mercury and Jupiter, space scientists will turn their attention to the sun, space outside of the ecliptic, and then to the more distant planets — Saturn, Uranus, Neptune, and Pluto. Little can be said today of what form these unmanned spacecraft will take, since they will come in a new decade which may also bring the permanent space station and electrical propulsion. These achievements will result in changes of most of the components of the spacecraft. The type of information needed about these planets, however, is similar to that sought from Venus and Mars.

Finally, when new forms of propulsion have been developed, tested, and proved reliable, and when all the problems of keeping man in space for extended periods have been resolved, manned exploration of the solar system will get under way. It is difficult to estimate with accuracy the date for the first planetary expedition. We must first await accumulation of all the data from the lunar exploration program and its attendant preliminary steps, and from the unmanned planetary and interplanetary probes. On the basis of current knowledge, it appears that a manned mission to Venus could not be undertaken before 1975, but "breakthroughs" in propulsion and other areas of intense research effort could change the estimate.

WILLIAM MEYERRIECKS

Beyond the Planets

THE accomplishments of the early years of the Space Age may have given an exaggerated impression of man's ability to "conquer" space. Man has entered space, survived, and in a few years he will set foot on the moon. These are tremendous achievements, but when we talk in terms of exploring the universe they pale into insignificance.

From man's first space flight until his landing on the moon, from six to ten years of concentrated scientific and engineering effort will be required. The reasons it takes so long have been broadly outlined. However, for each major problem area stated there are literally thousands of minor problems, too minute to be detailed here. Each must be solved before the moon voyage becomes a reality.

As man learns more about the universe, of which his planet, Earth, is so tiny a part, the pace of space exploration will accelerate. Knowledge may bring a great breakthrough which

CHAPTER 11

CROSS SECTION OF OUR GALAXY

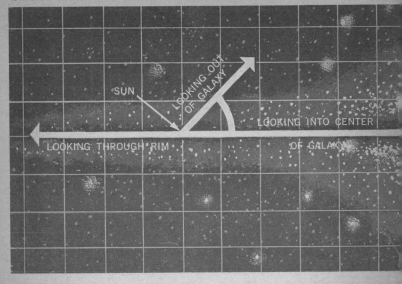

will permit travel beyond our solar system. Yet, even with the greatest predictable advances in space-flight techniques, the task appears all but insurmountable.

The Speed of Light

The barrier to exploration of the universe lies in the distances to the stars, distances so great that it is difficult for the human mind to grasp them. Even a *billion* miles is too puny a measure of distance in outer space; we must employ the light-year, or the distance light travels in one Earth calendar year. Light moves at a velocity of 186,300 miles per second, so a light-year is 186,300 times sixty seconds, times sixty minutes, times twenty-four hours, times 365 days, or almost six trillion (6,000,-000,000,000) miles.

At the speed of light, distant Pluto, the farthest planet in our solar system, is only six hours and forty-five minutes away.

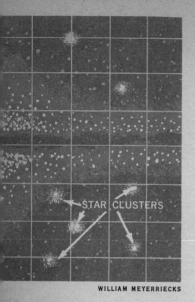

STAR CLUSTERS

Our star, sun, is but one of a hundred billion or more stars that make up our galaxy, the Milky Way. From edge to edge, the Milky Way is thought to measure 100,000 light-years. At the center, it is 10,000 light-years thick.

WILLIAM MEYERRIECKS

To get an idea of the distances involved in universal space, take a look at the familiar North Star, Polaris. Polaris is 300 light-years distant. The light you see left Polaris 300 years ago. Yet Polaris is practically a next-door neighbor.

The Milky Way

As a portion of the universe, our entire solar system is infinitesimally minute. Proxima Centauri, the star nearest our sun, is four and one-quarter light-years away. These two stars — our sun and Proxima Centauri — are members of a galaxy we call the "Milky Way," a grouping of an estimated *hundred billion* stars. The Milky Way is so immense that it would take a spacecraft moving at the speed of light 100,000 years to traverse its length.

The Milky Way galaxy itself is but one of about two dozen galaxies in what is called the "local" group. We can see the light from the Andromeda galaxy, another member of the local group — this light has been traveling through space for 700,000 years! And in the universe there are uncountable groups of galaxies, at distances so vast that even the light-year becomes an inadequate measurement.

The Barrier to Interstellar Exploration

Yet, according to currently accepted scientific theory, the speed of light is a limit beyond which no particle can be accelerated. Even if such a velocity were possible, it would take almost nine years to make a round trip to Proxima Centauri, the nearest star. If a particle of matter traveling at nearly the speed of light had started at one end of the Milky Way on the day Christ was born, it would not yet be one fiftieth of the way across the galaxy.

In the area of deep-universe travel, any speculation at this time is meaningless. Man simply does not have the knowledge to consider methods for real penetration of the universe. Whether we can ever achieve exploration of the universe must remain for the time being a suspended question. It will, most likely, take a new order of human intelligence even to contemplate the solutions to such an awesome problem, and no one can predict when man can reach that level of intelligence.

Yet, to the optimist, the feeling that interstellar and intergalactic travel will come is inescapable, scientific barriers aside. One has only to ponder all the "impossibles" which have already occurred. In discovering the New World, Columbus achieved the impossible, although some "scientific" opinion held that he would sail off the end of the Earth. Only a hundred years ago, flight itself was "impossible." As recently as 1945, in the enlightened twentieth century, a number of persons in positions to "know" stated authoritative opinions that the speed of sound — a mere 760 miles per hour — was an absolute limit to aircraft velocity. Today, *twice* the speed of sound is routine for military aircraft and within the decade airline passengers

And beyond our galaxy—there are others extending to the very edge of the visible universe, to the edge of imagination. Still, they beckon us.

will be flying at these speeds. And what of space flight itself — how recently was it "impossible"? Who knows what "impossibles" tomorrow's science will make routine?

Small as it is in terms of universal distance, our own solar system holds myriad secrets, the unlocking of which will provide a source of fascination and countless benefits to the generations privileged to live in this great age of science and technology. We have front row seats to witness the most dramatic adventure of all time, the exploration of solar space, and we may be alive to witness the sequel.

Ideas
for
Projects
and
Experiments

Invitation

YES, it's true you can't build your own Apollo or Explorer spacecraft. If you are wise, you will wait until you are an engineer to try to launch your own explosive-propelled rocket. But there are things you can do to join the teams of creative and inventive people who are having the fun and excitement of getting ready for space travel.

Begin now to look into the things which make space travel possible. Take some steps toward understanding the problems that must be solved to get a spacecraft through the Earth's atmosphere and back again without burning up. Find out what it really takes to have a spacecraft pull away from — or develop forces equal to — the Earthward attraction of gravity. Learn how difficult it is to balance forces acting on an object in such a way that it will move in a curved path.

You can learn to recognize some of the signposts that space navigators use to keep track of objects moving in space. Get to know the kind of curved paths that spacecraft are likely to travel.

The activities which follow have been developed by people who like to use their hands as well as their heads — by people who like to have the satisfaction of knowing they can build things that really work. And so can you!

Getting Through the Earth's Atmosphere

It is not easy for a man to leave the Earth's surface and

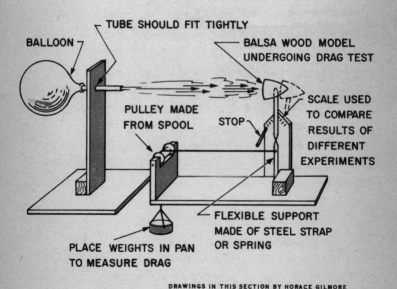

DRAWINGS IN THIS SECTION BY HORACE GILMORE

Figure 1. Device for drag experiments can be constructed of scrap. Compressed air or other gases can be used instead of balloon. Try models of different shapes.

climb through its atmosphere to arrive eventually in that mysterious environment known as space. The problems to be solved are almost as difficult as those a fish would encounter if it were to leave its water habitat and try to climb or fly into the air to live with the birds. Since it has neither wings for flying nor feet for crawling, a fish would have to propel itself while still in the water to such a great speed that its momentum would carry it through — for at least a brief visit into the air.

The faster an object moves through any fluid — such as air or water — the greater the resistance or *drag effect* the object encounters. In addition to speed, the drag on an object moving through a fluid depends upon the density of the fluid and the size, shape, smoothness, and other features of the object itself.

Figure 1 shows a device that you can build and use to study the effects of various factors on the drag of model spacecraft hulls of your own design.

Experiments can be planned using different shapes of test models, all of which have the same weight, or models of the same shape and dimensions but having different weights. Models that are identical except for the condition of their surfaces can be compared. The effects of different shapes of nose cones can be determined. You may try filling the balloon with carbon dioxide or some other gas to see if the density of the fluid makes any difference in the amount of drag it causes on one or more different spacecraft models.

If you want to specialize in the study of drag, the formula is $D = C_d \, \frac{1}{2}\rho \, V^2 \, A$. In words, the drag (D) of an object is equal to the drag coefficient (C_d) times one-half the fluid density (ρ) times the square of the velocity of the fluid (V^2) times the frontal area (A).

Pulling Away from the Earth's Gravity

When we think about the scientific problems of space travel, many things we take for granted here on Earth assume a new importance. Gravity is a good example. Can you imagine what a chaotic place the world would be if gravity could no longer be relied upon to keep things where they have been put? Although gravity seems at times to be a handicap, it has its desirable effects. Even the pole vaulter or high jumper is better off with gravity acting on him. He may have to give a mighty effort to get off the ground, but he would be in worse trouble clawing space madly to get down again if gravitational forces were to disappear.

Each time we step on a scale to see how much we weigh, we are measuring the pull Earth's gravity exerts on the mass of our bodies. But the true nature of gravitational force can be better described than explained. It is known that all objects in the universe are attracted to one another by a force that decreases as the objects become farther apart and increases if the total mass of the objects increases.

A change of distance between the center of Earth and the center of an object will result in a change of weight of the object. For example, an object that weighs 240 pounds on the surface of the Earth might weigh only sixty pounds if it were to be shot into space so far that it would be twice the distance from Earth's center. An object on Earth's surface is about 3,960 miles from the center of Earth. Using the previous example, can you calculate the weight of the object at 11,880 miles from Earth's surface?

Although airplanes travel through the atmosphere because of both the resistance and lift provided by the pressure of the air, spacecraft must be propelled by forces that act even where there is no air. Propulsion can be achieved by harnessing the so-called action-reaction principle. This is the same kind of action that causes a boat to be kicked away from you if you try to step away from it to shore without first securing it to a dock.

The action-reaction principle can be seen in the skittering of an inflated balloon when it is released. Try carving different shapes of "exit nozzles" to insert in the neck of a balloon to see if one shape is better than another in keeping the balloon moving longer or farther. Figure 2 suggests two shapes. The 15-45-degree nozzle is the shape that seems to be the best for actual rocket motors.

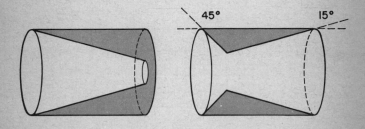

Figure 2. Carve different shapes of "exit nozzles" from balsa wood or plastic. Attach to balloons to determine effect of nozzle on gas release velocity, thrust.

The moon orbits constantly around the Earth; in a sense, it has pulled away from the Earth's gravity. As long as the gravitational attraction between the moon and Earth is balanced by the moon's orbital velocity, the moon, which is always falling toward the Earth, never reaches it. At the same time, being held in orbit by identical forces, the moon never wanders away.

To study the forces which act on an object that is moving in a circular path, drive a roundhead screw into a golf ball or hard rubber sponge ball. Tie strong twine or fishing line to the screw. Grasp the twine twelve inches from the ball. Whirl the ball fast enough to keep the ball "in orbit," that is, so that it will not fall toward your fingers when it reaches the top of its path. Count the number of circles it makes at the minimum speed during one minute.

Let go of the string while the ball is in orbit. Notice that the ball does not continue to circle but flies off in a straight-line tangent to the circle.

Now grasp the twine twenty-four inches from the center of the ball. Again whirl the ball at the slowest speed that will keep the ball in orbit and count the number of circles per minute. Make the same kind of count when the twine is thirty-six or forty-eight inches long. You will notice several things about the action of the ball, including the changing pull on your finger. Calculate the velocity for each orbit. Do you suppose the weight of the ball has anything to do with the number of circles per minute required to keep the ball in orbit?

Try the same experiment with the twine running through a spool. Attach a small weight to the end opposite the ball. Estimate the number of rotations per minute required to support the weight at various radii.

It is this balancing of gravitational force and the velocity of the ball that keeps objects in space from falling toward or away from other planets, the sun, or other stars.

To see how this works, cut a plywood disc the size of a twelve-inch phonograph record. In the center of this disc, drill

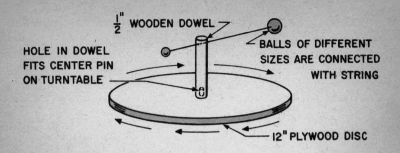

Figure 3. Here is device to explore relation between orbital velocity and gravity. Spin on turntable.

a hole large enough to take a three-inch length of half-inch dowel (Figure 3). Drill a horizontal hole through the upper end of the dowel. Before gluing the dowel to the plywood "record," drill a hole up through the center of the dowel so that the record can be placed over the pin on a record player and "played." Find two wooden, rubber, or plastic balls of different sizes. Pass a string through one ball, then through the horizontal hole at the top of the dowel, and through the second ball. Start the record player and see if you can balance one ball against the other so that the string moves neither way through the dowel. (These experiments will not work on a record changer, only on a turntable.)

You can use the plywood record for two more investigations. Fasten a rubber band to a golf ball or other small rubber or wooden ball. Change the speed of the record player, and see if there is a change in the distance the ball stretches the rubber band while it is turning.

Fasten a post near the edge of the disc (Figure 4). Hang a small ball from the top of the post. Observe the ball when the record is turning at various speeds. You will see that when gravi-

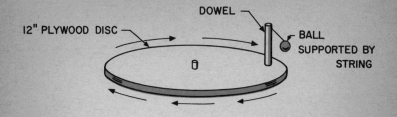

Figure 4. Plywood record is modified for more experiments.

tational forces alone act on the ball it simply hangs at the end of the string but when the proper speed of rotation is reached, the ball is kept suspended in "space."

Speed and Distance

An object moving over the surface of the Earth at about 25,000 miles per hour develops enough velocity to prevent it from falling to the Earth. Indeed, at this speed, the force developed is of sufficient magnitude so that the object can "escape" from the gravitational pull exerted by the Earth.

It is interesting to see how the speed of an object is related to the horizontal distance it covers before falling to the Earth's surface. Figure 5 shows a device that lets you study this relationship.

One of the most interesting things to see with your rocket launcher is the relationship between distance traveled by a model and the amount of force used to launch it. Measure the distance traveled by a model after it has been launched with various amounts of force. If you can devise a way to estimate the length of time the model spent in flight, you can divide the total distance by the time and obtain the average velocity or speed of the model. This may give you a good idea of what an escape velocity of 25,000 miles per hour really means.

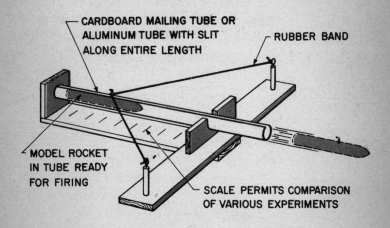

Figure 5. This device permits you to explore relation between flight distance and force at launch. With strobe light and camera you can also study ballistic paths. Can you figure out method to determine velocity?

Objects Moving In Curved Paths

The curved path or trajectories of spacecraft are likely to be more apparent to us than the curved paths of objects moving on or near the Earth's surface. In fact, such words as circles, ellipses, parabolas, and hyperbolas will be common words to space travelers. Figure 6 shows the shape of each of these curves.

It is interesting to see how each of these curves can be

produced by cutting a cone as shown in Figures 7 through 10. A cone can be made from modeling clay, balsa wood, or plaster of Paris. If clay or plaster is used, make a form by folding heavy paper into a cone and securing the edges with transparent tape. If the cone is filled with some material that "sets," remove the paper form just before it becomes hard, then cut the cone with a fine wire along the planes as indicated in the figures. By sawing the wire back and forth carefully, a smooth, clean cut can be made.

It is interesting to see what combinations of forces and

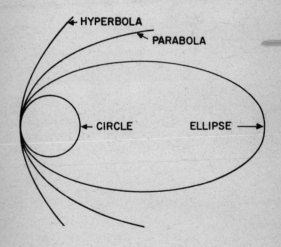

Figure 6. Path of space vehicle depends upon the velocity imparted by rockets through time last stage is fired. If velocity equals or exceeds escape velocity, path is open-ended parabola or hyperbola. Lower velocities result in elliptical or circular paths.

circumstances are required to cause an object to move in each of the different kinds of curved paths. To follow a circular path, for example, the forces acting on a moving object must act in such a way as to keep the object always the same distance from a point.

But what about the ellipse? How does an object manage to stay in that kind of path? You can answer this question if you simply draw an ellipse. Figure 11 shows how.

When you draw an ellipse you can see that the sum of the distances from a point (the moving pencil point) to two fixed points (the two pins) always remains the same because the circumference of the loop of string always remains the same length.

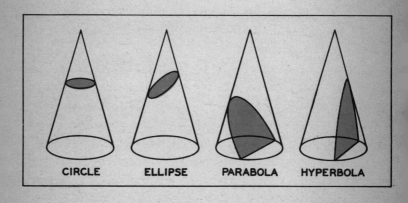

CIRCLE   ELLIPSE   PARABOLA   HYPERBOLA

Figures 7-10. The form and mathematical relationships of the curved paths of spacecraft can be studied in models cut from a cone. An analytical geometry text will give you formula for the curves.

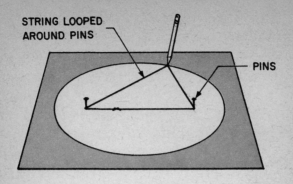

Figure 11. In drawing ellipse, sum of distances from moving pencil to two fixed pins remains constant.

The parabola is as easily described but is more difficult to draw. By description, an object will move in a parabolic path if it moves in such a way as to remain equidistant from a point and a fixed straight line.

If you draw a parabola by the method shown in Figure 12, you will see that the length of the string from the moving point (pencil) to a fixed point (pin) is always equal to the distance from the moving point to a fixed line (straight edge).

To understand how a spacecraft manages to stay in a circular, elliptical, or parabolic path, you must recognize that forces act on the moving spacecraft and create the same over-all effect as that which caused your pencil to follow a similar curved path when you drew these same curves. Of course, it takes better imagination to see fixed points and fixed lines in space than it takes to see pins or straight edges fixed to a drawing board.

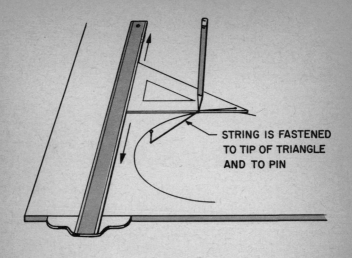

STRING IS FASTENED
TO TIP OF TRIANGLE
AND TO PIN

Figure 12. If you draw a parabola by the method shown above, you must take care to keep the string taut as the triangle is moved up and down straight edge.

To Find One's Way in Space

To find your way in any situation you need familiar landmarks or guideposts that are either always in the same place, or have predictable, regular movements. In space, directions and locations are established by using planets, the sun, or other stars as the "landmarks" and guideposts.

To be able to find and recognize the stars important for space navigation is not only necessary for anyone who hopes to find his way in space, but it is also fun for those who will spend all of their lives here on Earth. Astronomers have very accurate ways of locating a star at any instant in space. Because the apparent position of any star in the sky depends on where the observer is, the date, and the time the star is being observed, the methods used to locate a star are a bit complicated. Here is a device (Figure 13) you can build that will let you pin-

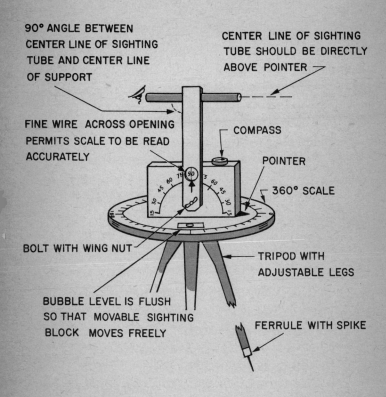

90° ANGLE BETWEEN CENTER LINE OF SIGHTING TUBE AND CENTER LINE OF SUPPORT

CENTER LINE OF SIGHTING TUBE SHOULD BE DIRECTLY ABOVE POINTER

FINE WIRE ACROSS OPENING PERMITS SCALE TO BE READ ACCURATELY

COMPASS

POINTER

360° SCALE

BOLT WITH WING NUT

TRIPOD WITH ADJUSTABLE LEGS

BUBBLE LEVEL IS FLUSH SO THAT MOVABLE SIGHTING BLOCK MOVES FREELY

FERRULE WITH SPIKE

Figure 13. Star finder requires two basic parts: one measures angle between horizon and star; the other measures angular displacement from true north. Note that 360° scale is fixed.

point any star that is normally visible from your own spot on the Earth's surface.

One of the easiest and most valuable things to do with your star finder is to measure the altitude of the North Star. This not only tells you the latitude of your location but also lets you line your star finder toward true north. You can then set the zero degree mark of the full circle scale on true north and swing the viewing tube around to mark the location of any other star. Here are some questions you can answer with the help of your star finder:

Is there any other star in the sky that stays at the same altitude and direction the way the North Star does? Suppose a star is exactly east of you at an altitude of 40° (angular elevation above the horizon) at 8:00 P.M. Where will this star be at 9:00 P.M.?

When you locate the position of a star one night at a particular time, will the star be in exactly the same spot the next night at the same time? How long does it take for a star that appears to be in a position directly overhead to move around the sky and return to the same position?

You may find it interesting to team up with other people who live in other parts of the country and compare what you can find out about the stars with your star finder. You can explore such questions as: What is the altitude of a star as observed by someone in California when its altitude as observed in New York is 65 degrees? How far south of you is a person who observes the altitude of the North Star to be 10 degrees less than it is where you observe it?

Here's another question: Two people who live several miles apart, but at the same latitude, observe the same star at the same instant. Can the observed difference in altitude be used to determine how far the two observers were from each other at the time of the observation?

Your star finder can be used to make interesting observations about the movement of the moon and the planets. There is, of course, much more to be learned before you will be able to use the positions of the stars as guideposts for travel in space. But finding the answers to easy questions is the best way to get ready for the difficult ones.

You will very probably make your first acquaintance with the stars by learning to recognize the constellations and then associating the important stars with their constellations. One of the best ways to become familiar with star constellations is to prepare two-inch by two-inch photographic slides of the constellations. Project the slides on a wall or ceiling, and observe them until they are quite familiar. Here is a way to make a set of constellation slides.

Load a camera with the fastest film available. Films such as Ansco Hypan or Agfa Isopan Record require exposures of about fifteen seconds. Attach the camera to a tripod and aim it at the constellation you want to have for your slide. Focus at infinity and with the shutter set on "bulb" or "time," expose for about fifteen seconds. Longer exposure times yield streaks rather than sharp points.

After your film has been returned from the processor, punch very small holes through the film at the points where the stars appear. Try to match the brightness of the star with the size of the hole. When you project the constellations, these holes will let light come through. When you make slides, record the day, time, and altitude for each constellation.

More Things to Do

Until you can see familiar objects removed from the effects of atmospheric pressure, humidity, gravity, and the other environmental factors on Earth, you will probably never realize how much these factors affect their properties. You may not realize, for example, that many things retain their shape because they are being constantly bombarded by air particles, or that a liquid evaporates slowly because its molecules only occasionally find room among the other molecules above the surface of the liquid. If there were an absence of air above the liquid, might not the liquid evaporate almost instantly?

Perhaps you have already seen what will happen to a syrup or varnish can if it is filled with steam, closed tightly, and then the steam is suddenly condensed to water. With only a little water in the can and air under very low pressure, pressure on the outside completely crushes the can. The next time you see this demonstration, slip a small air-filled rubber or plastic ball into the can and see what happens.

Because people need continuous supplies of oxygen-rich air to breathe, water to drink, food to eat, and heat to keep them warm, life in space holds many problems. In addition, waste materials must be eliminated and most people seem to need familiar sights and company if they expect to stay in good mental health. To bring all of these problems into the open, perhaps you can design a large poster or chart to show how many of the things we have in a modern home to maintain our health and comfort that would not work at all in a space environment that lacks air pressure, gravity, and humidity. Are there some things that would work even better in space than they do here on Earth? How about mercury vapor or fluorescent lights?

The first efforts to place spacecraft in orbit and to make manned explorations in space are among the important events of the twentieth century. You may want to keep an event-by-event chart showing the date of each satellite and space probe as it was shot into space.

One type of a chart could be made by using aluminum clothesline wire that can be easily cut and bent to form the orbital paths of spacecraft. Don't expect, however, to show the whole path followed by those objects which apparently went into orbit around the sun.

Since so many people know how much fun it is to make scale models of interesting and famous aircraft, all we will do here is to mention the similar fun you can have in making authentic scale models of the Explorers, Pioneers, Atlases, Saturns, and all of the other rockets and spacecraft that are helping man add space to his conquered frontiers.

As you look forward to travel in space, you doubtlessly think about the meteors and meteorites which whizz constantly through space. Meteors are interplanetary debris that enter Earth's gravitational field and are drawn toward its surface. They sometimes become visible when heated to incandescence by the friction of the atmosphere. Meteorites are large or small masses which survive their fiery trip through the atmosphere and land on the Earth's surface. Astronomers estimate that approximately 185,000,000 meteors large enough to leave visible trails streak across the skies each twenty-four-hour period. Most of the meteorites which reach the Earth are mere specks but the weight of a day's catch has been estimated at over one ton.

You may combine meteor hunting with practice in identifying the constellations or watching for the passage of a new satellite. Or, you can combine your photographing of star constellations with an attempt to catch a "falling star" on film. If you try to photograph a meteor, load your camera with fast film. Find a spot where stray lights from houses, cars, or aircraft won't fog your film, then point your camera toward the sky. Secure the camera firmly to a tripod or other support, open the shutter, and leave it open for several hours. When the film is developed, you may find a meteor's trail cutting across the circular star trails. Be patient; you can expect only about one meteor to appear on your photograph for each hundred hours of exposure time. You may have somewhat better luck during the Perseid meteor showers that are visible in the northern hemisphere during late summer.

Berkner, Lloyd V., and Odishaw, Hugh, editors, *Science in Space*. New York, McGraw-Hill Book Company, Inc., 1961; 458 pp., illustrated. Presents a review of the new scientific opportunities offered by space science. Directed to research workers and also may be of interest to general readers concerned with the national space effort.

Bizony, M. T., editor, *The Space Encyclopaedia*. New York, E. P. Dutton and Company, 1960. Details of satellites, missiles, and upper atmosphere research.

Buchheim, Robert W., *et al., Space Handbook*. New York, Random House, 1959; 330 pp., illustrated. A complete and comprehensive guide to the present and foreseeable future state of space flight and exploration of the universe, prepared by the author and staff of the Rand Corporation for the House Committee on Astronautics and Space Exploration in 1959 and revised for publication.

Clark, Arthur C., *The Exploration of Space*. New York, Harper and Brothers, 1951, 1959; 190 pp. Describes the why and how of astronautics.

DuBridge, Lee A., *Introduction to Space*. New York, Columbia University Press, 1960; 93 pp. A brief but clear review of what has been achieved in the conquest of space.

Lapp, Ralph, *Man and Space: The Next Decade*. New York, Harper and Brothers, 1961; 184 pp., illustrated.

Leavitt, William, *et al., The Space Frontier,* revised edition. Washington, D. C., National Aviation Education Council, 1961; 32 pp., illustrated. A description of space and a summary of man's efforts to explore space. A glossary and a log of U.S. and Soviet satellites and space probes are included.

Ley, Willy, *Rockets, Missiles, and Space Travel,* revised edition. New York, The Viking Press, 1961; 556 pp., illustrated. The definitive source book in the field. This newly revised edition includes facts that in earlier editions were only theories. Extensive annotated bibliography.

Thomas, Shirley, *Men of Space*, Vol. I. Philadelphia, Chilton Books, 1960; 234 pp., illustrated. Biographies of ten men who made possible advances in space flight: Ehricke, Goddard, Schriever, Stapp, Van Allen, von Braun, von Korman, Tsiolkovsky, von Neumann, and Yeager.

Thomas, Shirley, *Men of Space*, Vol. 2. Philadelphia, Chilton Books, 1961; 238 pp., illustrated. Biographies of Crossfield, Dornberg, Dryden, Dixon, Lovelace, Pickering, Ramo, Teller, Truax, and Whipple.

Trinklein, F. E., and Huffer, C. M., *Modern Space Science*. New York, Holt, Rinehart and Winston, Inc., 1961; 538 pp., illustrated. A textbook for the study of space science, based on astronomy but drawing upon all other fields of science related to space exploration.

1962 NASA Authorization, Pts. 1 and 2. Washington, D. C., Superintendent of Documents, U.S. Government Printing Office, 1961. Hearings before the Committee on Science and Astronautics and Subcommittees Nos. 1, 3, and 4, U.S. House of Representatives, Eighty-seventh Congress, First Session on H.R. 3238 and H.R. 6029 (superseded by H.R. 6874).

INDEX

INDEX

158

INDEX

JAMES J. HAGGERTY, JR.

For the past twenty years Mr. Haggerty has had his head in the clouds or above them, first as a combat navigator in World War II, and more recently as a writer and editor for aviation and space publications. In addition to his current work as editor of the *Aerospace Year Book,* Mr. Haggerty finds time to contribute encyclopedia articles on his favorite subjects and to write books. His other publications include *First Man in Space* (Duell, Sloan & Pearce, 1959) and *Project Mercury* (Scholastic Book Services, 1960).

JOHN H. WOODBURN

Currently teaching chemistry at Walter Johnson High School, Rockville, Maryland, Dr. Woodburn has also held positions at The Johns Hopkins University, Illinois State Normal University, and Michigan State University. He holds an A.B. degree from Marietta College, an M.A. from Ohio State, and a Ph.D. from Michigan State University.